W9-CPZ-934

OSTRACODA FROM THE GULF OF CALIFORNIA

The Memoir Series
of
The Geological Society of America, Inc.
is made possible
through the bequest of
Richard Alexander Fullerton Penrose, Jr.

The Geological Society of America, Inc.
Memoir 101

OSTRACODA FROM THE GULF OF CALIFORNIA

By

FREDERICK M. SWAIN

University of Minnesota, Minneapolis, Minnesota

1967

Made in the United States of America

PUBLISHED BY

THE GEOLOGICAL SOCIETY OF AMERICA, INC.

231 East 46th Street
New York, New York 10017

Design and Production by Technipress, Inc.
Manufactured by Port City Press, Inc.

ACKNOWLEDGMENTS

The writer is indebted to several people who helped with this study. Emily C. Mandelbaum and Peter L. Miller provided laboratory assistance for the study of samples of ostracode distribution. Special thanks are due June M. Gilby, who drew the appendages for the illustrations of species. Kenneth G. McKenzie provided valuable advice in taxonomic problems. Richard N. Benson and Olgerts L. Karklins assisted in photographic work. Ludmila Stupnitsky and Janet Anderson drafted the maps and typed the manuscript.

F. B. Phleger, T. H. van Andel, Jean P. Hosmer, and J. R. Curray of Scripps Institution of Oceanography, La Jolla, California, assisted in the procurement and loan of samples.

The research has been supported by Grant Nos. G-13933 and GB-1208 of the National Science Foundation.

Sincere appreciation is expressed for the assistance and financial support mentioned here.

CONTENTS

ILLUSTRATIONS

PLATES

FIGURES

CONTENTS

TABLES

ABSTRACT

This paper describes and illustrates 91 species of Recent Ostracoda from the Gulf of California; 42 species are newly described, 34 are previously described, and 15 are not given specific assignment.

Based on the collections studied here the following distributional associations of Gulf of California Ostracoda are noted:

1. Species generally distributed in the Gulf but occurring mainly nearshore in water less than 50 fathoms deep and on sandy mud or sand bottoms; or if present offshore, occurrences are in central and northern parts of Gulf in water up to several hundred fathoms deep and on sandy mud or mud bottom: 35 species.

2. Species restricted to nearshore localities in water less than 50 fathoms deep, on sand or sandy mud bottoms, and on both sides of Gulf: 17 species.

3. Species restricted to eastern marginal part of Gulf in water less than 50 fathoms deep and on sand, sandy mud, or muddy sand bottom: 7 species.

4. Species restricted to western marginal part of Gulf in water less than 50 fathoms deep, on sand, sandy mud, or muddy sand bottom: 15 species.

5. Species restricted to southern part of Gulf, offshore, in water down to 1,655 fathoms and on mud bottom: 1 species.

6. Species restricted to northern part of Gulf, offshore, in water down to 488 fathoms and on mud bottom: 3 species.

7. Species restricted to southwestern part of Gulf, nearshore, in waters less than 50 fathoms, and on sand or sandy mud bottom: 4 species.

8. Species restricted to southeastern part of Gulf, nearshore, in water less than 50 fathoms, and on sand or sandy mud bottom: 4 species.

9. Species characteristic of nonmarine or brackish water environments but in some instances found in offshore bottom sediments as a result of having been rafted on floating vegetation or other process of transportation: 7 species.

The possible sources of the ostracode fauna and migration paths of the species are briefly discussed.

1

INTRODUCTION

The Ostracoda described in this paper represent collections from the upper centimeter of sediment from about 200 stations in the Gulf of California (Figure 1a). The collections were obtained on the 1959 cruise

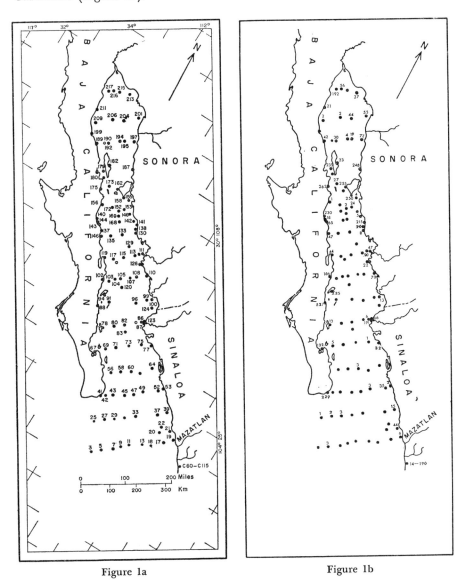

Figure 1a

Figure 1b

Figure 1. *Ostracode localities in Gulf of California.* (a) Numbers correspond to stations listed in Table 1; (b) Number of ostracode specimens in upper cm of sediment at each station

of the research vessel *E. W. Scripps* from Scripps Institution of Oceanography, under the direction of G. A. Rusnak (Table 1). Shore collections near Mazatlan, Sinaloa, were obtained in 1959 by a group from Scripps under the direction of J. R. Curray (Table 1).

TABLE 1. STATIONS, 1959 VERMILION SEA CRUISE, GULF OF CALIFORNIA, FROM WHICH OSTRACODA WERE OBTAINED [1] FOR THIS STUDY

Station	Latitude Deg.	Latitude Min. N	Longitude Deg.	Longitude Min. W.	Depth in fathoms	Bottom type
5	21	45.2	108	25.7	1572	Mud
7	21	59.0	108	6.1	1533	Mud
17	23	.0	106	44.0	340	Mud
19	23	12.8	106	29.7	8	Sand
20	23	12.0	107	.7	252	Mud
21	23	23.5	106	45.5	32	Mud
22	23	22.0	107	3.4	176	Mud
27	22	38.4	108	51.5	1580	Mud
33	23	14.5	107	59.6	1355	Mud
37	23	38.2	107	25.0	350	Sandy mud
39	23	50.0	107	9.5	21	Muddy sand
41	23	11.5	109	25.0	45	Sand
43	23	24.0	109	3.8	1235	Sandy mud
45	23	35.7	108	43.5	782	Muddy sand
47	23	45.3	108	28.0	1542	Mud
49	23	59.1	108	15.4	390	Mud
52	24	18.0	107	50.0	25	Sandy mud
53	24	23.5	107	41.4	8	Sand
56	23	57.5	109	31.5	950	Mud
58	24	8.3	109	15.1	750	Mud
60	24	20.5	108	58.0	1480	Mud
64	24	45.5	108	23.3	390	Mud
67	24	13.5	110	18.5	4	Sand
69	24	30.5	110	6.0	395	Mud
71	24	42.5	109	48.7	690	Mud
75	25	10.9	109	7.2	560	Mud
77	25	21.3	108	51.7	3	Sand
78	25	1.0	110	33.4	10	Sand
80	25	13.5	110	15.9	1100	Mud
82	25	26.6	109	58.5	1730	Mud
83	25	15.7	109	49.5	1545	Diatomite
86	25	46.5	109	32.5	30	Sandy mud
88	25	33.5	111	7.5	8	Gravel and sand
91	25	45.5	110	49.5	160	Muddy sand
94	25	58.4	111	7.6	4	Sand
96	26	6.5	110	13.5	877	Mud
99	26	26.0	109	45.5	190	Mud
100	26	32.2	109	36.8	38	Gravel and sand
102	26	16.5	111	23.8	6	Sand
103	26	20.0	111	13.4	192	Muddy sand
104	26	27.8	111	4.0	745	Mud
105	26	33.0	110	56.0	895	Hard clay
108	26	52.4	110	29.0	590	Mud
110	27	4.5	110	11.8	10	Sand
111	27	35.2	110	42.0	7	Hard clay
112	27	32.5	110	45.0	34	Hard clay
113	27	25.0	110	54.0	690	Mud
115	27	12.2	111	13.5	973	Mud
117	26	58.0	111	28.0	1082	Mud
119	26	52.5	111	45.0	31	Sand
123	25	52.5	109	27.5	5	Sandy mud
126	27	16.5	110	35.4	20	Sandy mud
129	27	32.6	111	14.1	655	Mud
130	28	1.0	111	18.1	62	Sandy mud
133	27	44.8	111	39.0	610	Mud
135	27	32.2	111	56.7	655	Mud
137	27	20.5	112	16.0	7	Muddy sand
138	28	8.0	111	20.3	17	Muddy sand
140	27	34.2	112	23.3	15	Shell and sand
141	28	14.1	111	24.9	10	Sand
142	28	17.7	111	33.0	15	Sand
143	27	37.5	112	32.0	10	Sand

TABLE 1 (*Continued*)

Station	Latitude Deg.	Latitude Min. N	Longitude Deg.	Longitude Min. W.	Depth in fathoms	Bottom type
144	27	42.0	112	37.5	75	Muddy sand
146	28	24.5	111	48.5	36	Sand
152	28	18.4	112	11.0	220	Sandy mud
153	28	25.0	112	3.1	18	Muddy sand
155	28	42.6	112	4.8	16	Muddy sand
156	28	11.7	112	48.4	7	Sand
158	28	43.5	112	18.0	17	Muddy sand
168	28	2.0	111	57.8	290	Sandy mud
169	28	10.0	112	6.0	296	Muddy sand
172	28	17.8	112	26.8	495	Diatomite
173	28	47.0	112	53.9	220	Muddy sand
175	28	33.4	113	7.1	7.5	Sand
179	29	3.2	113	20.3	488	Mud
180	28	56.0	113	33.8	14	Sand
182	29	16.0	113	17.9	6.7	Sand
187	29	39.2	112	34.5	13	Muddy sand
189	29	35.0	114	1.7	10	Sand
192	29	48.5	113	43.3	262	Mud
194	30	3.2	113	24.8	75	Muddy sand
197	30	16.2	112	58.5	28	Sandy mud
199	29	48.2	114	22.3	15	Muddy sand
201	30	56.0	113	16.8	13	Muddy sand
204	30	38.0	113	41.0	40	Muddy sand
206	30	28.5	114	.0	98	Sandy mud
209	30	10.0	114	27.7	35	Mud
211	30	29.4	114	37.6	10	Muddy sand
213	31	22.8	113	57.4	8	Sand
215	31	15.3	114	18.4	22	Muddy sand
216	31	11.1	114	28.2	18	Sandy mud
217	31	7.1	114	38.2	15	Sandy mud

C-60	Curray's Locality: Mangrove swamp near road from Tecuala to Novillero, at km 33 + 220 m from main highway to Mazatlan; this is a low between two cheniers; salinity 22.4‰
C-80	Curray's Locality: At edge of lagoon near road from Esquinapa to Las Cabras; salinity 42.0‰ at km 13 from Esquinapa, Sinaloa, Mexico; farther to north salt is being precipitated from this lagoon water
C-83	Curray's Locality: At km 11½ along same road in narrow lagoon between well-developed cheniers; surface of water covered with an algal slime; salinity 91.2‰
C-112	Curray's Locality: In lake 70 m from bank behind a submerged chenier covered with mangroves; Soft mud bottom with many shell fragments; Water depth 75 cm; salinity 5.8‰; location about 1 km east of Mexcaltitán
C-113	Curray's Locality: 250 m to N. 50 E.; water depth 50 cm; near clump of water hyacinths with roots to bottom
C-114	Curray's Locality: Same Lake 250 m to N. 50 E.; water depth 38 cm
C-115	Curray's Locality: Same lake 250 m farther on same course, about 50 m from other bank, which represents a submerged, mangrove-covered chenier; water depth 35 cm; mud at least 7 m thick and very soft; no sand encountered by probe

[1] A number of other stations examined (Fig. 1b) yielded no Ostracoda.

The upper centimeter of each of the core samples was preserved in neutralized formalin and returned to Scripps Institution, where, in F. B. Phleger's laboratory they were stained with Rose Bengal solution for detection of living specimens, sieved free of clay, and studied for Foraminifera. After the foraminiferal counts had been made, about 200 of the 241 marine samples obtained on the 1959 cruise were studied for ostracode distribution. The species were subsequently described and illustrated.

The illustrations of the species have been arranged on the plates and in the text to conserve as much space as possible. They are in neither biological nor alphabetical order.

References cited in the synonymies are not included in "References Cited" unless used in "Relationships" (new species) or "Remarks" (old species).

DISTRIBUTION OF OSTRACODA IN GULF OF CALIFORNIA

The geology and oceanography of the Gulf of California are described elsewhere (van Andel and Shor, 1964). Most of the area of the Gulf is characterized by an offshore, relatively deep water environment that rather strikingly limits the distribution of most of the Ostracoda to a narrow belt around the margin and around the islands. Oceanographic data as related to ostracode distribution are summarized in Table 2.

The Ostracoda from two bays on the eastern side of the Gulf were described by Benson and Kaesler (1963), who recognized 16 species and subspecies, 8 of which were newly described.

The present investigation shows that most of the hundred-odd ostracode species of the Gulf are rather widely distributed around the margin and around the islands and occur in offshore sediments in many instances. Many of the specimens found in offshore sediments probably were washed out from shallower depths. The number of specimens obtained at each locality is given in Figure 1b.

The following distributional patterns have been recognized in the material studied.

GENERAL DISTRIBUTION

The following species are more or less generally distributed in the Gulf but are found mainly at nearshore localities in the southern Gulf or, if present offshore, are found at localities mainly in central and northern parts of the Gulf. The depths at which the species occur ranges from about 1 fathom or less to several hundred fathoms. The bottom at the nearshore stations of less than 100 fathoms depth is variably sand, gravel and sand, muddy sand, or sandy mud, with sandy bottoms predominating. The following species are characteristic of these localities:

Ambostracon glauca (Skogsberg)
Argilloecia sp. (northern Gulf only)
Aurila conradi californica Benson and Kaesler
Bairdia fortificata Brady
Bairdia simuvillosa Swain sp. nov.
Basslerites thlipsuroidea Swain sp. nov.
Bythocypris leroyi Swain nom. nov. (northern Gulf only)
Cativella dispar Hartmann
C. unitaria Swain sp. nov.
Costa? cf. *variabilocostata seminuda* van den Bold
Cushmanidea pauciradialis Swain sp. nov.
Cytherella ovularia Swain sp. nov.
Cytheropteron assimiloides Swain sp. nov.
C. caboensis Swain sp. nov.

7

TABLE 2. OCEANOGRAPHIC DATA ON GULF OF CALIFORNIA AFTER RODEN AND GROVES (1959) AND THEIR RELATIONSHIP TO DISTRIBUTION OF OSTRACODA

Part of Gulf	Temperature		Salinity		Avg. O₂ ml/l	Seasonal variation ml/l	Relationship to ostracode distribution
	Avg. °C	Seasonal variation °C	Avg. ‰	Seasonal variation ‰			
Surface water, general Gulf	24.3	14.9–31.1	~35.4	34.9–36.0	~4.8	3.4–6.8	Generally favorable for diverse ostracode populations in shallow water; abundance tends to be greatest in upwelling areas along coasts
Water at depth of 100 m, northern Gulf	~17	14–20	~35.2	<35.2–35.3	2.5	2.8	Benthonic ostracodes relatively common; typical species are *Cytheropteron caboensis* sp. nov. and *Parakrithe* ? sp.
Water at depths of 500–1000 m in Ballenes Trench near Isla de la Guarda	~12	12–13	~35	34.9–35	<1.5	~1.5	Not generally favorable for benthonic ostracodes, but following seem typical of trench: *Argilloecia* sp., *Bairdia fortificata* Brady, *Bythocypris leroyi* nom. nov., *Costa* cf. *variabilocostata seminuda* Bold, *Cytheromorpha* aff. *warneri* Howe and Spurgeon, *Cytheropteron assimiloides* sp. nov., *Cytheropteron caboensis* sp. nov., *Krithe producta* Brady, *Paracypris franquesoides* sp. nov., *Paracytherois* cf. *fischeri* (Sars)
Surface water, central Gulf	~25	18–30	~35.3	35.2–35.4	~5	4–6	Favorable for nearshore benthonic ostracodes, especially in upwelling areas.
Water at depth of 100 m, central Gulf	~17	14–20	~35	34.8–35.2	~3	2–4	Benthonic ostracodes fairly common; typical species are *Costa* cf. *variabilocostata seminuda* Bold, *Cytheropteron assimiloides* sp. nov. and *Pteroloxa guaymanensis* sp. nov.
Water at depths of 500–1000 m in central Gulf	~7	5–9	~34.55	<34.55–34.6	~0.2	0.2–0.5	Not favorable for benthonic ostracodes
Surface water, southern Gulf	~26	21–30	~35	34.8–35.2	5+	4–5+	Nearshore benthonic ostracode species common to abundant.
Water at depth of 100 m in southern Gulf	~17		~34.7	34.5–35.3	~0.5	0.2–2	Favorable for nearshore benthonic ostracodes, but large populations of individuals are rare; greatest abundance in upwelling areas along coasts; representative species: *Bairdia fortificata* Brady, *Bairdia bradyi* van den Bold, *Basslerites* sp.?, *Costa* cf. *variabilocostata seminuda* Bold, *Paracypris franquesoides* sp. nov. Howe and Chambers, *Pterygocythereis cuevasensis* sp. nov.
Water at depths of 500–1000 m in southern Gulf	~7	4–9	~34.6	34.55–34.6+	~0.2	0.1–0.5	Unfavorable to most Ostracoda
Water at depths of 2000 m in southern Gulf	~2	?	~34.6	?	1.5	?	Ostracoda rare to absent at most stations sampled; radiolaria very abundant, diatoms abundant; *Miracythere* sp., *Krithe producta* Brady, and *Cytheropteron caboensis* sp. nov. are ostracode species found there

C. *ventrokurtosa* Swain sp. nov.
Cytherura johnsonoides Swain sp. nov.
Cytherura johnsonoides Swain sp. nov., subspecies a
Kangarina quellita Coryell and Fields
Krithe producta Brady
K. sp. immature
?Leguminocythereis corrugata LeRoy
Megacythere punctocostata Swain sp. nov.
Monoceratina bifurcata Puri
Orionina pseudovaughani Swain sp. nov.
Paracytheridea granti LeRoy
"*Paracytheridea*" *simplex* Swain sp. nov.
Pellucistoma scrippsi Benson
Perissocytheridea meyerabichi (Hartmann) (reworked offshore in some areas, perhaps by floating vegetation).
Pterygocythereis delicata (Coryell and Fields)
Pumilocytheridea sp.
Puriana pacifica Benson
Trachyleberidea? sp.
Xestoleberis hopkinsi Skogsberg
X. nana Brady
X. parahowei Swain sp. nov.

BOTH MARGINS OF GULF, NEARSHORE

The following species are found in shallow waters, less than 50 fathoms deep, and on gravel and sand, sand, muddy sand, or sandy mud bottoms:

Ambostracon vermillionensis Swain sp. nov.
Bairdia verdesensis LeRoy
Caudites rosaliensis Swain sp. nov.
Cytherelloidea californica LeRoy
C. sanlucasensis Swain
Cytheropteron altatensis Swain sp. nov.
C. dobladoensis Swain sp. nov.
Cytherura laconica Swain sp. nov.
C. paracostata Swain sp. nov.
Hemicythere californiensis LeRoy
Loxoconcha lenticulata LeRoy
L. tamarindoidea Swain sp. nov.
Loxocorniculum sculptoides Swain sp. nov.
Macrocyprina pacifica (LeRoy)
Mutilis confragosa (Edwards)
Sclerochilus contortellus Swain sp. nov.

EASTERN SIDE OF GULF, NEARSHORE

Several of the species studied were found only at nearshore localities along the eastern side of the Gulf in water less than 50 fathoms deep, typically on sand or sandy mud bottom:

Aglaiocypris virgenensis Swain sp. nov.
Cushmanidea? sp. immature
Cytheroma sp. aff. "*Microcythere*" *gibba* Müller
Cytherura bajacala Benson

Parakrithella oblonga Swain sp. nov.
Pteroloxa guaymanensis Swain sp. nov.
Xiphichilus tenuissimoides Swain sp. nov.

WESTERN SIDE OF GULF, NEARSHORE

A group of species was found in the present collections in shallow water only on the western side of the Gulf in water less than 50 fathoms deep, on gravel and sand, sand, or muddy sand bottoms:

Aurila convergens Swain sp. nov.
A. sp. immature
Costa? sanfelipensis Swain sp. nov.
Cushmanidea guardensis Swain
Hemicythere sp.
Paracypris franquesoides Swain sp. nov.
P. politella Swain sp. nov.
Paracytheridea pichelinguensis Swain sp .nov.
Paradoxostoma cf. *hodgei* Brady
P. micropunctata Swain sp. nov.
Paradoxostomatid ostracodes, unidentifiable
Pterygocythereis? cuevasensis Swain sp. nov.
Pumilocytheridea vermiculoidea Swain sp. nov.
Loxoconcha? emaciata Swain sp. nov.
Trachyleberidea tricornis Swain sp. nov.

SOUTHERN GULF, OFFSHORE

One species was found only in the southern offshore area south of Baja California at 1,655 fathoms in mud bottom:

Miracythere? sp.

NORTHERN GULF, OFFSHORE

Three of the species were found only in offshore stations down to 488 fathoms on mud bottom, in the northern Gulf:

Cytheromorpha? sp. aff. *C. warneri* Howe and Spurgeon
Cytherois cf. *fischeri* (Sars)
Microcythere? sp.

SOUTHWESTERN GULF, NEARSHORE

A few species were found only in stations close to shore in water ranging down to 45 fathoms on sand or mud bottom:

Ambostracon sp. immature
Bairdia bradyi van den Bold
Basslerites delrayensis LeRoy
Cytherella parapunctata Swain sp. nov.

SOUTHEASTERN GULF, NEARSHORE

Two of the species were found only nearshore along the southeastern side of the Gulf in water down to 32 fathoms and on mud, sand, and sandy mud bottom:

Basslerites sp.
Cytherelloidea cf. *umbonata* Edwards

BRACKISH WATER OR FRESHWATER

The following species were found in J. R. Curray's collections from brackish, hyperhaline, and freshwater lagoonal and deltaic locations south of Mazatlan, Sinaloa, together with a few species of this type that had been reworked to offshore localities:

Cladoceran ephippia
Cyprideis currayi Swain sp. nov. (reworked offshore in some areas)
Cyprinotus unispinifera Furtos (a few specimens in offshore samples probably transported by floating vegetation)
Darwinula yaquensis Swain sp. nov. (reworked offshore in a few instances)
Limnocythere sanctipatricii Brady and Robertson
Perissocytheridea meyerabichi (Hartmann) (commonest occurrence of species)
Potamocypris mazatlanensis Swain sp. nov. (a few specimens reworked offshore)
Stenocypria australia Swain sp. nov. (a few specimens found in offshore samples)

POSSIBLE ORIGINS OF THE OSTRACODE FAUNA

Of the more than 90 species recorded in this paper 61, or about 66 percent, are restricted in their known distribution to the Gulf of California or in a few cases to the west coast of Baja California. Of these, about 11 species have closely related species in the Caribbean—Gulf of Mexico region.

About 19 species, or roughly 21 percent of the Gulf of California species, are found elsewhere along the Pacific coast of North or Central America. Only about 5 species, or 5 percent of the fauna, are found in the Caribbean or Gulf of Mexico region; but when the 11 related species are taken into account, about 16 species, or 17 percent of the ostracode fauna, seem to have their origins in the Caribbean—Gulf of Mexico area.

Seven of the species, or about 8 percent of the fauna, appear to have more general distribution or are found in the North Atlantic, western Pacific, Mediterranean, or other areas.

Thus the ostracode population of the Gulf of California is more than half represented by indigenous species, with contributions of a little more than 20 percent from the Pacific coastal region and less than 20 percent from the Caribbean region.

The collection comprises mostly dead specimens that may not have lived at the localities where they were collected. The extent to which they may have been reworked seaward cannot be determined. Benson and Kaesler (1963) described the ecology of several nearshore species from the eastern side of the Gulf, based mainly on empty shells. Several of their species are in offshore stations of the present collection. In general, the marine Ostracoda of the collection are shallow-water, nearshore forms, probably associated with algae as a food supply. After death, the empty shells were swept outward to greater or lesser distances and came to rest in sand or sandy mud bottoms for the most part. Some of the species, however, such as the more highly winged Cytheropterons, probably are more common away from the surf zone and are indicative of the outer neritic zone of this area.

Samples of a group of closely spaced stations extending from nearshore out to 200 fathoms near Las Tres Marias Islands were examined for ostracodes with the hope of obtaining more detailed information about some of the species. Ostracoda were relatively rare in all this group of samples and served only to substantiate the nearshore character of the Gulf assemblage as a whole. Further ecologic studies of the Ostracoda of this area would probably best be confined to the bays and the littoral zones where individuals as well as species seem to be in greatest abundance.

The percentage distribution of the individual ostracode species of the total ostracode population at the stations from which samples were studied is shown in Figures 2 to 29. Owing to bunching of species at certain stations, it proved cumbersome to arrange the species alphabetically on the maps. A key to the maps is therefore given below:

Aglaiocypris virgenensis Swain sp. nov. (Fig. 2)
Ambostracon glauca (Skogsberg) (Fig. 7)
A. vermillionensis Swain sp. nov. (Fig. 3)
A. sp. immature (Fig. 6)
Argilloecia sp. (Fig. 2)
Aurila convergens Swain sp. nov. (Fig. 2)
A. conradi californica Benson and Kaesler (Fig. 4)
A. sp. immature (Fig. 2)
Bairdia cf. *fortificata* Brady (Fig. 23)
B. bradyi van den Bold (Fig. 2)
B. simuvillosa Swain sp. nov. (Fig. 8)
B. verdesensis LeRoy (Fig. 23)
Basslerites delrayensis LeRoy (Fig. 19)
B. thlipsuroidea Swain sp. nov. (Fig. 7)
B. sp. (Fig. 19)
Bythocypris leroyi Swain nom. nov. (Fig. 5)
Cativella dispar Hartmann (Fig. 28)
C. unitaria Swain sp. nov. (Fig. 28)
Caudites rosaliensis Swain sp. nov. (Fig. 25)
Costa? sanfelipensis Swain sp. nov. (Fig. 6)
C.? cf. *variabilocostata seminuda* van den Bold (Fig. 8)
Cushmanidea guardensis Swain sp. nov. (Fig. 4)
C. pauciradialis Swain sp. nov. (Fig. 5)
C.? sp. (Fig. 6)
Cyprideis currayi Swain sp. nov. (Fig. 15)
Cyprinotus unispinifera Furtos (Fig. 19)
Cytherella ovularia Swain sp. nov. (Fig. 8)

C. parapunctata Swain sp. nov. (Fig. 6)
Cytherelloidea californica LeRoy (Fig. 9)
C. sanlucasensis Swain sp. nov. (Fig. 9)
C. sp. (Fig. 6)
Cytherois cf. *fischeri* (Sars) (Fig. 9)
Cytheroma? sp. aff. *"Microcythere" gibba* Müller (Fig. 8)
Cytheromorpha sp. aff. *C. warneri* Howe and Spurgeon (Fig. 14)
Cytheropteron altatensis Swain sp. nov. (Fig. 11)
C. assimiloides Swain sp. nov. (Fig. 10)
C. caboensis Swain sp. nov. (Fig. 11)
C. dobladoensis Swain sp. nov. (Fig. 9)
C. ventrokurtosa Swain sp. nov. (Fig. 10)
C. sp. (broken) (Fig. 14)
Cytherura bajacala Benson (Fig. 14)
C. johnsonoides Swain sp. nov. (Fig. 11)
C. laconica Swain sp. nov. (Fig. 14)
C. paracostata Swain sp. nov. (Fig. 3)
Darwinula yaquensis Swain sp. nov. (Fig. 13)
Hemicythere californiensis LeRoy (Fig. 24)
H. sp. a immature (Fig. 24)
H. sp. b (Fig. 13)
Kangarina cf. *quellita* Coryell and Fields (Fig. 20)
Krithe producta Brady (Fig. 7)
?Leguminocythereis corrugata LeRoy immature (Fig. 12)
Limnocythere sanctipatricii Brady and Robertson (Fig. 16)
Loxoconcha? emaciata Swain sp. nov. (Fig. 16)
L. lenticulata LeRoy (Fig. 15)
L. tamarindoidea Swain sp. nov. (Fig. 15)
Loxocorniculum sculptoides Swain sp. nov. (Fig. 12)
Macrocyprina pacifica (LeRoy) (Fig. 21)
Megacythere punctocostata Swain sp. nov. (Fig. 18)
Miracythere sp. (Fig. 19)
Monoceratina bifurcata Puri (Fig. 20)
Mutilus confragosa (Edwards) (Fig. 25)
Orionina pseudovaughani Swain sp. nov. (Fig. 17)
Paracypris franquesoides Swain sp. nov. (Fig. 21)
P. politella Swain sp. nov. (Fig. 21)
Paracytheridea granti LeRoy (Fig. 22)
P. pichelinguensis Swain sp. nov. (Fig. 22)
"P." simplex Swain sp. nov. (Fig. 17)
Paracytherois? perspicilla (Benson and Kaesler) (Fig. 18)
Paracytheropteron sp. immature (Fig. 18)
Paradoxostoma cf. *hodgei* Brady (Fig. 24)
P. micropunctata Swain sp. nov. (Fig. 18)
Paradoxostomid ostracodes, unidentifiable (Fig. 16)
Parakrithe? sp. immature (Fig. 13)
Parakrithella oblonga Swain sp. nov. (Fig. 18)
Pellucistoma scrippsi Benson (Fig. 23)
Perissocytheridea meyerabichi (Hartmann) (Fig. 24)
Potamocypris mazatlanensis Swain sp. nov. (Fig. 20)
Pteroloxa guaymanensis Swain sp. nov. (Fig. 5)
Pterygocythereis? cuevasensis Swain sp. nov. (Fig. 26)
P. delicata (Coryell and Fields) (Fig. 26)
Pumilocytheridea vermiculoidea Swain sp. nov. (Fig. 12)

P. sp. (Fig. 5)
Puriana pacifica Benson (Fig. 19)
Sclerochilus? contortellus Swain sp. nov. (Fig. 3)
Stenocypria australia Swain sp. nov. (Fig. 16)
Trachyleberidea tricornis Swain sp. nov. (Fig. 27)
T. sp. (Fig. 27)
Xestoleberis hopkinsi Skogsberg (Fig. 29)
X. cf. *nana* Brady (Fig. 29)
X. parahowei Swain sp. nov. (Fig. 28)
Xiphichilus tenuissimoides Swain sp. nov. (Fig. 25)

The type specimens will be housed in the University of Minnesota Paleontological Collections.

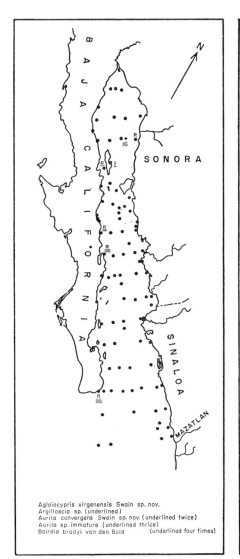

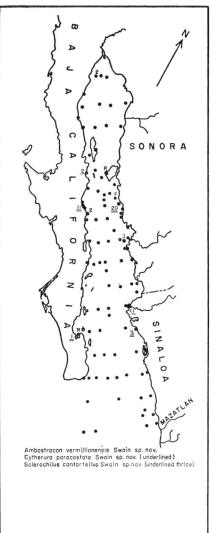

Figure 2   Figure 3

Figure 2. *Distribution of* Aglaiocypris virgenensis *Swain sp. nov.,* Argilloecia *sp.,* Aurila convergens *Swain sp. nov., A. sp., and* Bairdia bradyi *van den Bold in Gulf of California, in percent of ostracode population at each station or in actual number of specimens indicated by appropriate letter (R = 4 or less).*

Figure 3. *Distribution of* Ambostracon vermillionensis *Swain sp. nov.,* Cytherura paracostata *Swain sp. nov.,* Sclerochilus? contortellus *Swain sp. nov., and S. nasus* Benson *in Gulf of California, in percent of ostracode population at each station or in actual number of specimens indicated by appropriate letter (R = 4 or less).*

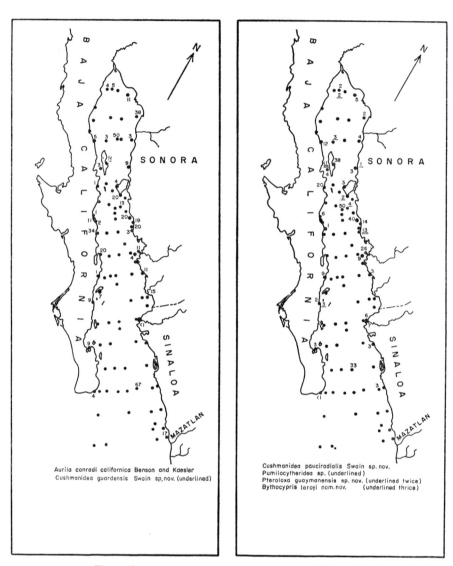

Figure 4

Figure 5

Figure 4. *Distribution of* Aurila conradi californica *Benson and Kaesler and* Cushmanidea guardensis *Swain, sp. nov. in Gulf of California, in percent of
ostracode population at each station.*

Figure 5. *Distribution of* Bythocypris leroyi *Swain nom. nov.,* Cushmanidea pauciradialis
Swain sp. nov., Pumilocytheridea *sp., and* Pteroloxa guaymanensis *Swain sp.
nov. in Gulf of California, in percent of ostracode population at each station.*

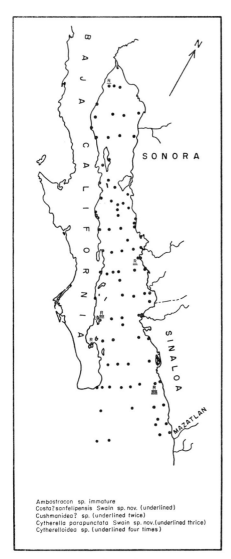
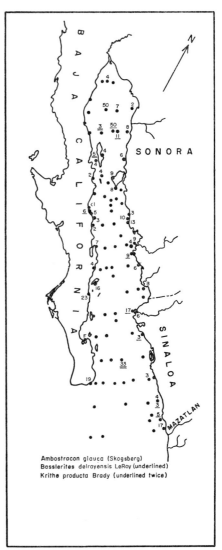

Figure 6   **Figure 7**

Figure 6. *Distribution of* Ambostracon *sp.,* Costa? sanfelipensis *Swain sp. nov.,* Cushmanidea? *sp.,* Cytherella parapunctata *Swain sp. nov., and* Cytherelloidea *sp. in Gulf of California, in actual number of specimens indicated by appropriate letter (R = 4 or less).*

Figure 7. *Distribution of* Ambostracon glauca *(Skogsberg),* Basslerites delrayensis *LeRoy, and* Krithe producta *Brady in Gulf of California, in percent of ostracode population at each locality or in actual number of specimens indicated by appropriate letter (F = 5–9).*

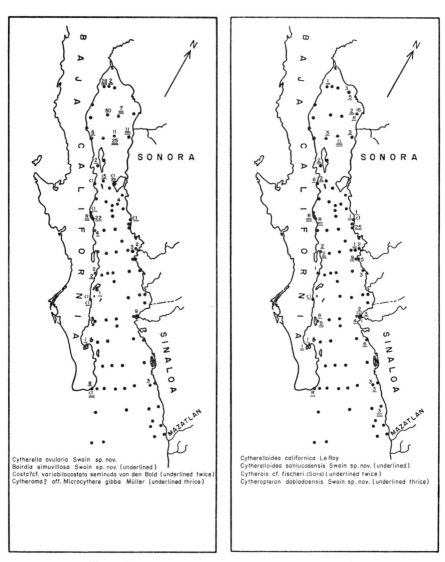

Figure 8   Figure 9

Figure 8. *Distribution of* Cytherella ovularia *Swain sp. nov.,* Bairdia simuvillosa *Swain sp. nov.,* Costa? cf. variabilocostata seminuda *van den Bold, and* Cytheroma? *aff. "Microcythere" gibba Müller in Gulf of California, in percent of ostracode population at each locality or in actual number of specimens indicated by appropriate letter (R = 4 or less).*

Figure 9. *Distribution of* Cytherelloidea californica *LeRoy,* C. sanlucasensis *Swain sp. nov.,* Cytherois *cf.* fischeri *Sars, and* Cytheropteron dobladoensis *Swain sp. nov. in Gulf of California, in percent of ostracode population at each locality or in actual number of specimens indicated by appropriate letter (R = 4 or less).*

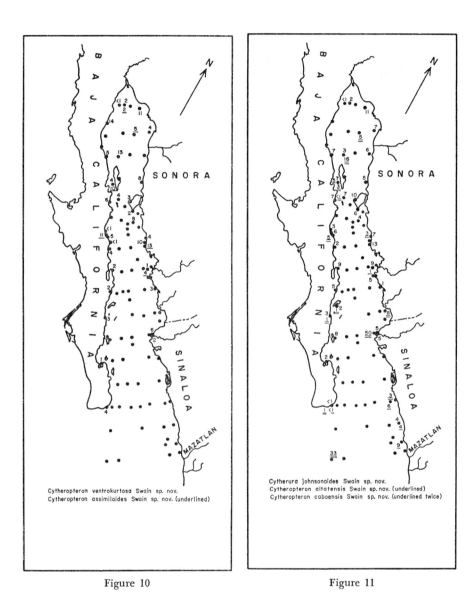

Figure 10

Figure 11

Figure 10. *Distribution of* Cytheropteron ventrokurtosa *Swain sp. nov. and* C. assimiloides *Swain sp. nov. in Gulf of California, in percent of ostracode population at each locality.*

Figure 11. *Distribution of* Cytherura johnsonoides *Swain sp. nov.,* Cytheropteron altatensis *Swain sp. nov., and* C. caboensis *Swain sp. nov. in Gulf of California, in percent of ostracode population at each locality.*

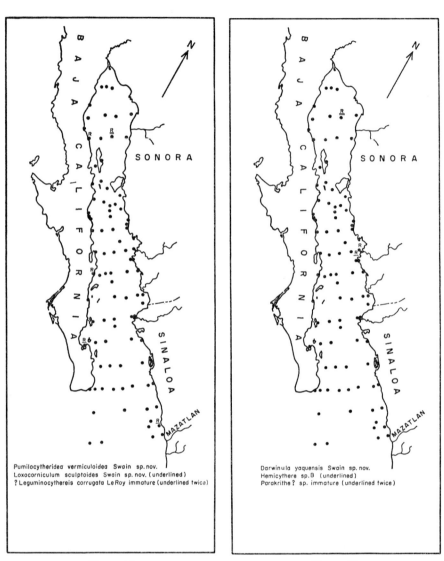

Figure 12   Figure 13

Figure 12. *Distribution of* Pumilocytheridea vermiculoidea *Swain sp. nov.,* Loxocorniculum sculptoides *Swain sp. nov., and* ?Leguminocythereis corrugata *LeRoy in Gulf of California, in actual number of specimens indicated by appropriate letter (R = 4 or less).*

Figure 13. *Distribution of* Darwinula yaquensis *Swain sp. nov.,* Hemicythere *sp. b, and* Parakrithe? *sp. in Gulf of California, in actual number of specimens indicated by appropriate letter (R = 4 or less).*

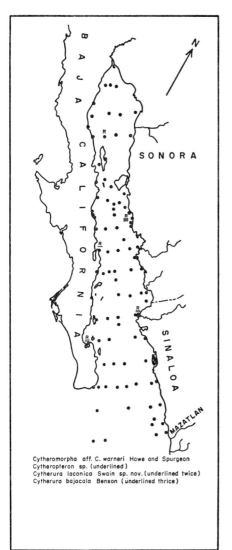

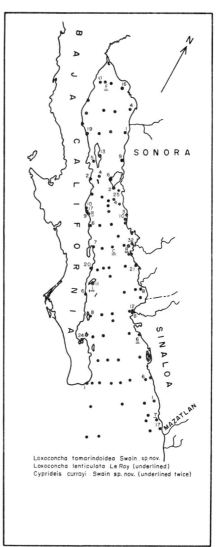

Figure 14   Figure 15

Figure 14. *Distribution of* Cytheromorpha *sp. aff.* C. warneri *Howe and Spurgeon,* Cytheropteron *sp.,* Cytherura laconica *Swain sp. nov., and* C. bajacala *Benson in Gulf of California, in actual number of specimens at each locality indicated by appropriate letter* (R = 4 *or less*).

Figure 15. *Distribution of* Loxoconcha tamarindoidea *Swain sp. nov.,* L. lenticulata *LeRoy, and* Cyprideis currayi *Swain sp. nov. in Gulf of California, in percent of ostracode population at each locality or in actual number of specimens indicated by appropriate letter* (R = 4 *or less,* F = 5-9, C = 10-19).

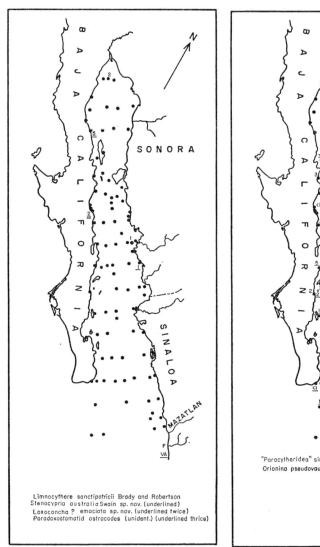

Figure 16

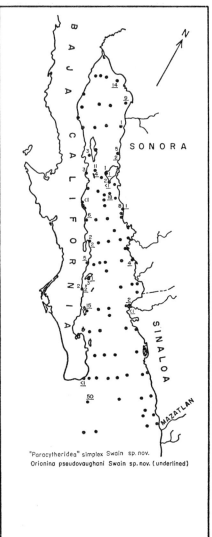

Figure 17

Figure 16. *Distribution of* Limnocythere sanctipatricii *Brady and Robertson,* Stenocypria australia *Swain sp. nov.,* Loxoconcha? emaciata *sp. nov., and* paradoxostomatid ostracodes, *otherwise unidentifiable, in Gulf of California, in percent of specimens indicated by appropriate letter* (F = 5–9, VA = 50 or more).

Figure 17. *Distribution of* "Paracytheridea" simplex *Swain sp. nov. and* Orionina pseudovaughani *Swain sp. nov. in Gulf of California, in percent of ostracode population at each locality.*

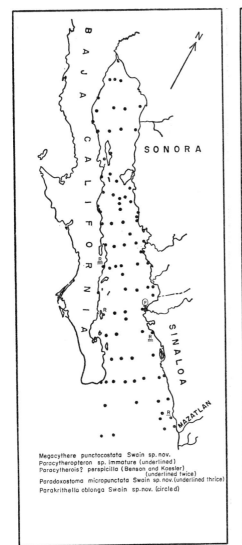

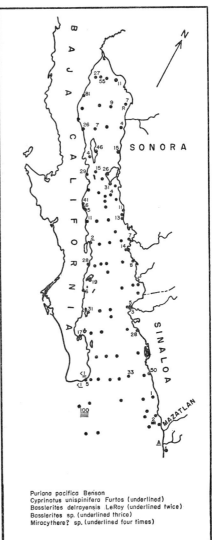

Figure 18   Figure 19

Figure 18. *Distribution of* Megacythere punctocostata *Swain sp. nov.,* Paracytheropteron *sp.,* Paracytherois? perspicilla *(Benson and Kaesler),* Paradoxostoma micropunctata *Swain sp. nov., and* Parakrithella oblonga *Swain sp. nov. in Gulf of California, in actual number of specimens indicated by appropriate letter (R = 4 or less, F = 5–9).*

Figure 19. *Distribution of* Puriana pacifica *Benson,* Cyprinotus unispinifera *Furtos,* Basslerites delrayensis *LeRoy, B. sp., and* Miracythere? *sp. in Gulf of California, in percent of ostracode fauna at each locality or in actual number of specimens indicated by appropriate letter (A = 20–49).*

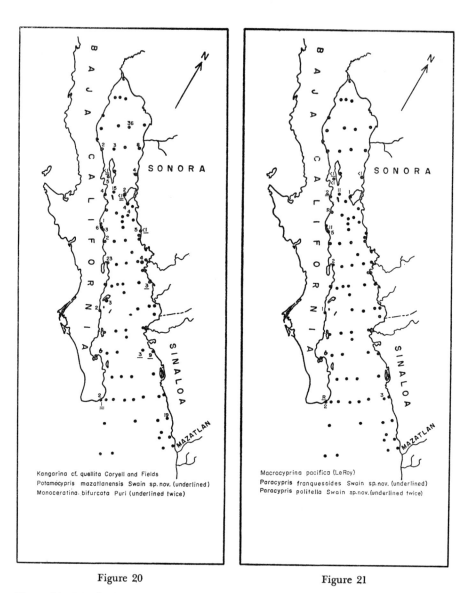

Figure 20

Figure 21

Figure 20. *Distribution of* Kangarina *cf.* quellita *Coryell and Fields,* Potamocypris mazatlanensis *Swain sp. nov., and* Monoceratina bifurcata *Puri in Gulf of California, in percent of ostracode population at each locality.*

Figure 21. *Distribution of* Macrocyprina pacifica *LeRoy,* Paracypris franquesoides *Swain sp. nov., and P.* politella *Swain sp. nov. in Gulf of California, in percent of ostracode population at each locality or in actual number of specimens indicated by appropriate letter (R = 4 or less).*

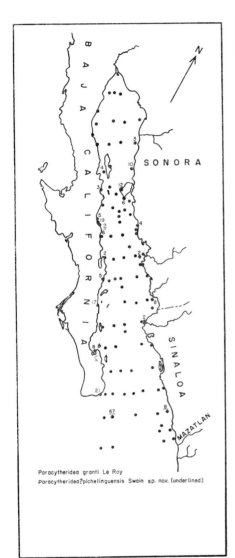

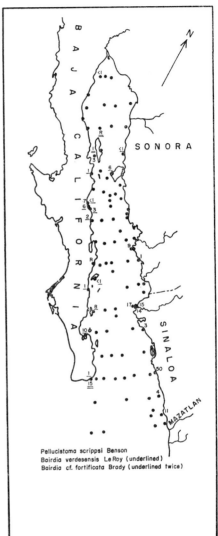

Figure 22   Figure 23

Figure 22. *Distribution of* Paracytheridea granti *LeRoy and* P. pichelinguensis *Swain sp. nov. in Gulf of California, in percent of ostracode population at each locality or in actual number of specimens indicated by appropriate letter* (R = 4 or less).

Figure 23. *Distribution of* Pellucistoma scrippsi *Benson,* Bairdia verdesensis *LeRoy, and* B. cf. fortificata *Brady in Gulf of California, in percent of ostracode population at each locality or in actual number of specimens indicated by appropriate letter* (R = 4 or less).

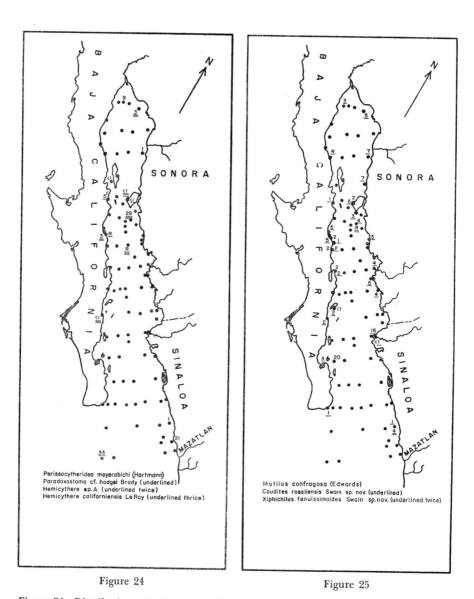

Figure 24   Figure 25

Figure 24. *Distribution of* Perissocytheridea meyerabichi *(Hartmann),* Paradoxostoma cf. hodgei *Brady,* Hemicythere *sp. a, and* H. californiensis *LeRoy in Gulf of California, in percent of ostracode population at each locality or in actual numbers indicated by appropriate letter (R = 4 or less).*

Figure 25. *Distribution of* Mutilus confragosa *(Edwards),* Caudites rosaliensis *Swain sp. nov., and* Xiphichilus tenuissimoides *Swain sp. nov. in Gulf of California, in percent of ostracode population at each locality or in actual number of specimens indicated by appropriate letter (R = 4 or less, F = 5–9).*

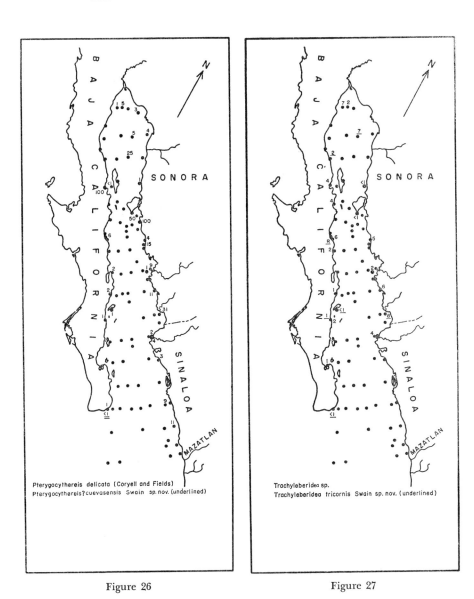

Figure 26   Figure 27

Figure 26. *Distribution of* Pterygocythereis delicata *(Coryell and Fields) and* P. cuevasensis *Swain sp. nov. in Gulf of California, in percent of ostracode population at each locality.*

Figure 27. *Distribution of* Trachyleberidea? *sp. and* T. tricornis, *Swain sp. nov. in Gulf of California, in percent of ostracode population at each locality or in actual number of specimens indicated by appropriate letter (R = 4 or less).*

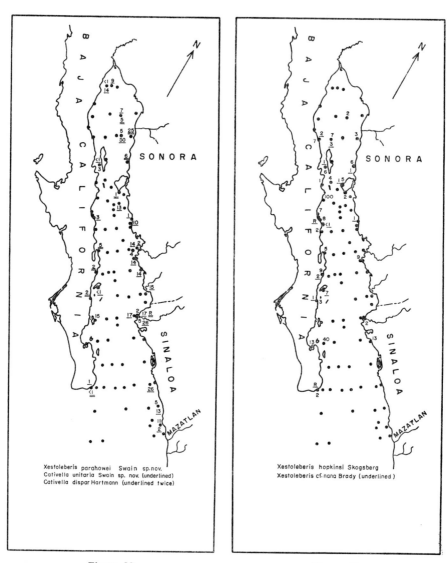

Figure 28   Figure 29

Figure 28. *Distribution of* Xestoleberis parahowei *Swain sp. nov.,* Cativella unitaria *Swain sp. nov., and* C. dispar *Hartman in Gulf of California, in percent of ostracode population at each locality or in actual number of specimens indicated by appropriate letter (R = 4 or less).*

Figure 29. *Distribution of* Xestoleberis hopkinsi *Skogsberg and* X. *cf.* nana *Brady in Gulf of California, in percent of ostracode population at each locality or in actual number of species indicated by appropriate letter (R = 4 or less).*

SYSTEMATIC DESCRIPTIONS

Subclass OSTRACODA Latreille, 1806
Order PODOCOPIDA Müller, 1894
Suborder PLATYCOPINA Sars, 1866
Family CYTHERELLIDAE Sars, 1866
Genus *Cytherella* Jones, 1849

Cytherella ovularia Swain sp. nov.
(Fig. 30b; Pl. 1, fig. 7)

Shell ovate in side view, highest medially; dorsal margin convex, slightly truncate on either side of position of greatest height; ventral margin gently convex; anterior margin broadly and uniformly curved; posterior margin somewhat narrower, subtruncate below. Right valve larger than and extends slightly beyond edge of left anteriorly. Valves moderately convex, greatest convexity posteromedian. Anteromiddorsal surface of valves slightly depressed; general surface weakly and sparsely pitted.

Hinge line of right valve with simple groove for reception of edge of left valve. Muscle scar an oval dorsomedian area composed of many longitudinally elongate spots on either side of a vertical midline. Free margin of right valve with selvage groove into which fits edge of left. Normal canals widely spaced over general surface of valve.

Length of holotype right valve 0.53 mm, height 0.36 mm, convexity of valve 0.18 mm.

RELATIONSHIPS: The ovate form, weak dorsomedian surface depression of valves, and sparse weak pitting are characteristics of the species. *Cytherella polita* Brady (1880, p. 172) is similar in shape but lacks surface pitting and sulcation and *C. punctata* Brady (1880, p. 174) is sulcate but more elongate and more densely pitted than *C. ovularia* sp. nov.

OCCURRENCE: Gulf of California, Station 52, depth 25 fathoms, in sandy mud; Station 88, depth 8 fathoms, in gravel and sand; Station 102, depth 6 fathoms, in sand; Station 111, depth 7 fathoms, in hard clay; Station 112, depth 34 fathoms, in hard clay; Station 123, depth 5 fathoms, in sandy mud; Station 153, depth 18 fathoms, in muddy sand; Station 175, depth 7.5 fathoms, in sand; Station 195, depth 75 fathoms, in sandy mud.

NUMBER OF SPECIMENS STUDIED: 9

Cytherella parapunctata Swain sp. nov.
(Fig. 30a; Pl. 7, fig. 1)

?*Cytherella punctata* BRADY, 1880, Challenger Reports, pt. 3, p. 125, Pl. 44, fig. 4e–g, not a–d

Shell subovate-subelliptical in side view, highest just posterior to midlength; dorsal margin gently convex, with steep posterior slope; somewhat sinuous anteromedially; ventral margin nearly straight; anterior margin broadly and uniformly curved; posterior margin more narrowly curved, extended medially, truncate above. Valves moderately convex, greatest convexity posteromedian. Dorsomedian broad shallow sulcus extends from margin nearly to midheight; general surface densely reticulate; in marginal areas reticulations arranged concentrically; dorsal, anterior, and anterior half of ventral margin with very narrow rim.

Hinge surface of right valve consists of a groove, broadest and deepest anteriorly, into

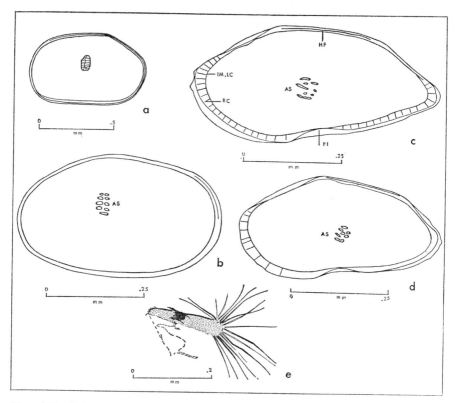

Figure 30. Cytherella *and* Bairdia. (a) *Cytherella parapunctata* Swain sp. nov., Gulf of California, Station 78, interior of left valve; (b) *C. ovularia* Swain sp. nov., Gulf of California, Station 111, interior of right valve; (c–e) *Bairdia simuvillosa* Swain sp. nov.; (c, d) Interior of two right valves; (e) Brush-shaped organ, Gulf of California, Station 143. Abbreviations: *aht*, anterior hinge tooth; *ahs*, anterior hinge socket; *pht*, posterior hinge tooth; *phs*, posterior hinge socket; *if*, interterminal hinge furrow; *ib*, interterminal hinge bar; *as*, adductor muscle scar; *ds*, diductor muscle scar; *lc*, line of concrescence; *im*, inner margin; *rc*, radial canals; *nc*, normal canals; *mnc*, marginal normal canals that resemble radial canals in *Cytherelloidea; pi*, podocopid incurvature of midventral margin; *hf*, hinge furrow

which fits edge of left valve. Muscle scar lies at ventral end of median sulcus and consists of about 16 spots arranged in two close-packed vertical rows.

Length of holotype right valve 0.80 mm, height 0.43 mm, convexity 0.18 mm.

RELATIONSHIPS: The punctate surface, truncated posterodorsal margin, and weak sulcus distinguish this species. *Cytherella punctata* Brady is more equal-ended but has similar surface ornamentation. Specimens referred to *C. punctata* from the South Pacific off New Zealand (Brady, 1880, p. 175) are narrower posteriorly and may represent the new species. The shape of this species is that of *Platella* Coryell and Fields (= *Cytherella* by Moore et al., 1962).

OCCURRENCE: Recent, Gulf of California, Station 78, depth 10 fathoms, sand bottom.
NUMBER OF SPECIMENS STUDIED: 3

Genus *Cytherelloidea* Alexander, 1929

Cytherelloidea californica LeRoy
(Fig. 31; Pl. 1, figs. 1, 11)

Cytherelloidea californica LeRoy, 1943, Jour. Paleontology, v. 17, p. 357, Fig. 2b, Pl. 58, figs. 32–35; Benson 1959, Kansas Univ. Paleont. Contr., Arthropoda, article 1, p. 39, Pl. 1, fig. 2, Pl. 8, fig. 13

Shell subelliptical in side view, highest slightly behind midlength; dorsal margin gently convex; ventral margin nearly straight to slightly concave medially; anterior margin broadly and nearly uniformly arcuate; posterior margin more narrowly curved, strongly truncate below, extended above. Left valve slightly larger than right, overlapping and extending beyond right along free margins. Valves compressed, greatest convexity posteromedian.

An anterior, submarginal, broad, low rim rises near anterior cardinal angle and along venter continues posteriorly as a much narrower rim; dorsomedially and about one-sixth from dorsal margin a low, narrow ridge occupies middle half of valve; medially a somewhat sinuous longitudinal ridge extends about four-fifths of shell length; ventro-medially a third, nearly straight longitudinal ridge also extends about four-fifths of shell length. General surface weakly and rather coarsely pitted.

The appendages have not been described previously.

Antennule with broad proximal segment sharply geniculate with respect to second, also very broad podomere; third podomere wedge-shaped, fourth through seventh podomeres short and become progressively narrower distally; second podomere with three anterior distal clawlike setae, remaining segments with three, two, two, and two anterior distal clawlike setae respectively; third, fourth, and through sixth podomeres each with single posterior distal setae; setae of seventh podomere form terminal claws; no exopodite observed.

Antenna with first two joints uniramous, sharply geniculate, next podomere biramous, segmented, from distal margins of which extend numerous long, bristlelike setae; both inner and outer rami have only two segments visible.

Mandible truncated obliquely at cutting edge, bearing five to six small teeth and a small anterior seta; palp two-jointed, distal segment small, with one seta, proximal one with comblike row of long setae along inner face and a single large spine near proximal end; no setose basal lamella observed.

Protopod of maxilla with two small posterior and one large anterior masticatory lobes, each bearing small distal spines; endopodite a palp of three segments each bearing clawlike setae ventrally and the whole with a comblike row of small setae; respiratory plate short and broad with long, weakly feathered setae.

First thoracic leg incompletely seen, palp biramous, consists of small two-segmented and larger two-segmented outer rami; each ramus with two or three terminal claws; respiratory plate broadly lobate, with about ten large, unfeathered setae.

Caudal ramus extending lamellalike from segmented posterior end of body, ramal lamella with six to ten flattened spines, each of which narrows to a seta terminally.

Length of figured right valve 0.60 mm, height 0.33 mm, convexity of valve 0.14 mm.

REMARKS: Although the internal structures were not observed, the form and surface ornament are similar to *Cytherelloidea californica* LeRoy. Typical *C. californica* has broader ridges and has a more weakly punctate surface but is probably conspecific with the Gulf of California specimens.

OCCURRENCE: Station 111, at 7 fathoms, hard clay bottom. The species was described from the Lomita Marl (Pleistocene) of southern California and also occurs in modern bays of that area (LeRoy, 1943, p. 357).

NUMBER OF SPECIMENS STUDIED: 5 (1 living)

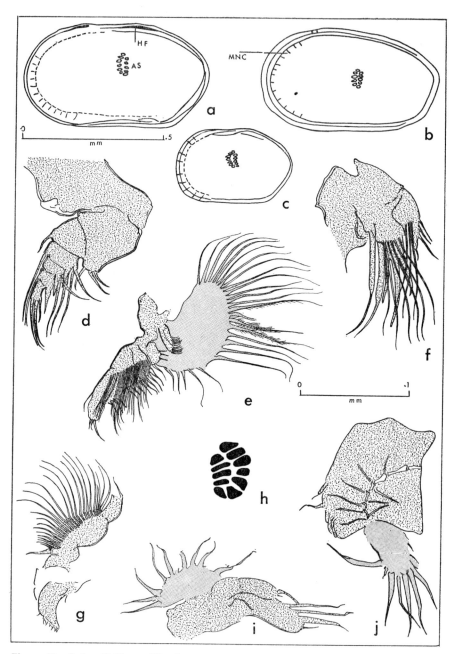

Figure 31. Cytherelloidea californica *LeRoy, Gulf of California, Station 111.* (a–c) Interiors of an adult and two immature right valves, Gulf of California,
Station 201; (d) Antennule; (e) Maxilla and respiratory lobe; (f) Antenna
(? incomplete); (g) Mandible and palp; (h) Adductor muscle scar; (i) First
thoracic leg; (j) Furca

Cytherelloidea sp.
(Pl. 7, figs. 2a–c)

Right valve subelliptical; dorsal margin slightly sinuous, subparallel to straight venter; anterior margin broadly and uniformly curved; posterior margin broadly curved, truncate above; valve compressed. A narrow rim lies parallel to and within anterior margin; ventral longitudinal submarginal ridge connects with anterior rim and terminates near posterior end in a node; middorsally a narrow short ridge connects with ventral side of end of anterior rim; posterodorsally another short ridge connects with ventral side of end of middorsal ridge and terminates near posterior end in a second elevated node; posterior nodes connected by a short vertical ridge; general surface otherwise smooth.

Hinge of right valve formed of simple edge of valve; muscle scar lies slightly dorsal to middle and consists of about five longitudinally elongate scars arranged in an oval spot.

Length of figured specimen 0.67 mm, height 0.37 mm, convexity of valve 0.12 mm.

REMARKS: The arrangement of ridges on this form is similar to that of *C. umbonata* Edwards (1944, p. 506) from the Upper Miocene of North Carolina, but the shell of that species is pitted. *C. tewarii* van den Bold (1963, p. 372) from the Upper Miocene of Trinidad is similar in general form and ornamentation but differs in details of the surface ridges.

OCCURRENCE: Recent, Gulf of California, Station 52, depth 25 fathoms, sandy mud bottom.

NUMBER OF SPECIMENS STUDIED: 1

Cytherelloidea sanlucasensis Swain sp. nov.
(Pl. 7, figs. 3a–c)

Shells strongly dimorphic, subovate to subelliptical in side view, highest anteromedially; dorsal margin in male shells sinuous to straight, in female shells nearly straight to slightly convex; ventral margin concave medially in males, nearly straight to very slightly concave posteromedially in females; anterior margin broadly curved; posterior margin narrower, truncated medially in males, slightly extended above and truncated below in females. Valves subequal, the right slightly larger, compressed, most convex posteromedially in males, posteroventrally in females.

Anterior and ventral margins with ridge that is relatively broad anteriorly, narrow midventrally; middorsal surface of shell with oblique ridge slanted toward anterior; posteromiddorsal surface with short longitudinal ridge that has a bulbous posterior expansion, bends ventrally to join a similar but longer ventral longitudinal ridge that also has a bulbous posterior expansion; inner flank of anterior marginal ridge, and to a lesser extent the other ridges, bears ten or more perpendicular, narrow spurs that define small pits.

Hinge margin of right valve consists of edge of valve that fits into groove in left valve; muscle scar a dorsomedially placed circular spot in which lie other markings not clearly preserved.

Length of holotype shell 0.58 mm, height 0.30 mm, convexity 0.20 mm.

RELATIONSHIPS: In shape and pattern of surface ridges, this species is similar to *Cytherelloidea umbonata* Edwards (1944, p. 506) from the Miocene of the southeastern U.S., but in that species the valve surface is more generally pitted than in the present species. The same is true of *C. californica* LeRoy (1943, p. 357) of the Pliocene and Recent of California.

OCCURRENCE: Recent, Gulf of California, Station 41, depth 45 fathoms, sand bottom; Station 52, depth 25 fathoms, sandy mud bottom; Station 201, depth 13 fathoms, muddy sand bottom; Station 213, depth 8 fathoms, sand bottom.

NUMBER OF SPECIMENS STUDIED: 15

Suborder PODOCOPINA Sars, 1866
Superfamily BAIRDIACEA Sars, 1888
Family BAIRDIIDAE Sars, 1888
Genus *Bairdia* McCoy, 1844

Bairdia simuvillosa Swain sp. nov.
(Figs. 30c, d; 32, 43a; Pl. 1, figs. 2a–f, 8)

Bairdia sp. aff. *B. verdesensis* LeRoy. BENSON, 1959, Kansas Univ. Paleont. Contr., Arthropoda, article 1, p. 42, Pl. 1, fig. 6. Pl. 8, fig. 16

Shell subtriangular-sublanceolate in side view, highest about one-third from anterior end; dorsal margin moderately to strongly convex, angulated anteromedially, straightened in front of and behind position of greatest height; ventral margin slightly concave to nearly straight medially; anterior margin rounded, extended above, subtruncate below; posterior margin pointed, strongly extended ventrad of midheight, truncate above. Left valve a little larger than right, valves moderately convex, greatest tumidity median. Surface of shell smooth except for scattered pits that mark sites of pore canals from which extend long bristles.

Hinge consists of a groove in posteromedian dorsal slope of left valve into which fits corresponding rabbeted edge of right; inner lamellae narrow, line of concrescence and inner margin separate; adductor muscle scar a slightly anteromedian, subcircular group of 10 to 12 spots.

Antennule with seven podomeres; proximal segment large and flattened; second segment shorter and narrower, with a long ventral distal seta; remaining segments short and progressively narrower distally; ultimate three each with two very long swimming setae.

Antenna with six podomeres; proximal three broad and flattened, each with a long dorsal seta and second and third with double or triple ventral setae; fourth and fifth podomeres long and narrow, with distal setae; sixth podomere very short, with three distal curved claws.

Mandible with five terminal long teeth, each of which is faintly serrate terminally; palp three-segmented, sharply geniculate; proximal segment with distal setae; second segment with four setae; distal segment with four terminal claws.

Protopod of maxilla with four narrow, strongly produced masticatory lobes, each sharply curved distally and with one to three setose terminal claws; maxillary endopodite palp comprises slightly extended ridge with six long setae; vibratory plate not clearly observed but large, lobate, and with long, feathered setae.

First, thoracic leg with four podomeres and terminal claw; proximal podomere with five or six long distal spines; next three podomeres with single short anterior distal spines; rounded vibratory plate attached to base of protopodite posteriorly.

Second and third legs also four-segmented with distal setae and terminal claw as in first leg.

Furca bears four setae on dorsal side, terminal claws very unequal, proximal one much longer; a third small penultimate seta near distal end of furca.

Length of holotype right valve 0.60 mm, height 0.33 mm, convexity 0.13 mm.

RELATIONSHIPS: The outline of the species is the same as the forms referred to by Benson (1959, p. 42) and differs from *B. verdesensis* LeRoy in lacking spines on the posteroventral margin of adult shells. *B. villosa* Brady (1880, p. 50) is similar in general outline and hirsute shell but is less elongate and has a more convex dorsum.

OCCURRENCE: Gulf of California, Station 143, depth 10 fathoms, sand bottom; Station 41, depth 45 fathoms, sand bottom.

NUMBER OF SPECIMENS STUDIED: 25 + (1 living)

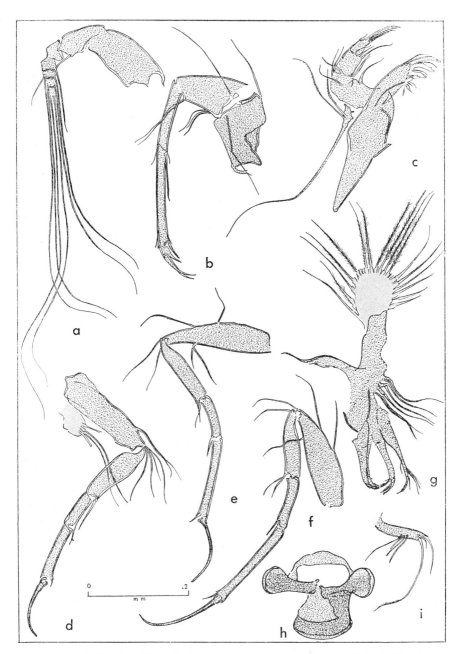

Figure 32. Bairdia simuvillosa *Swain sp. nov., Scammon Lagoon, Baja California.* (a) Antennule; (b) Antenna; (c) Mandible and palp; (d) First thoracic leg and part of palp; (e) Second thoracic leg; (f) Third thoracic leg; (g) Maxilla and respiratory lobe; (h) Jaw, (i) Furca

Bairdia verdesensis LeRoy
(Fig. 33; Pl. 1, figs. 6a–d)

Bairdia verdesensis LeRoy, 1943, Jour. Paleontology, v. 17, p. 358, Figs. 2f', g'; Pl. 60, figs. 5–9

The characteristic features of the shell of this species are: subtriangular outline, strongly convex umbonate dorsum; gently convex venter straightened medially, rounded anterior margin extended medially and truncate above, pointed posterior margin, strongly extended below; punctate surface; a few small spines on posteroventral margin of left valve.

Length of figured left valve specimen (Pl. 1, fig. 6c) 0.81 mm, height 0.50 mm, convexity of valve 0.23 mm.

OCCURRENCE: The figured specimens are from station 67, Gulf of California, depth 4 fathoms, sand bottom; and from Station 143, depth 10 fathoms, sand bottom; also from Station 41, depth 45 fathoms, sand bottom; Station 78, depth 10 fathoms, sand bottom; Station 94, depth 4 fathoms, sand bottom; Station 137, depth 7 fathoms, muddy sand bottom; Station 144, depth 75 fathoms, muddy sand bottom; Station 162, depth 13 fathoms, sand bottom; Station 175, depth 7.5 fathoms, sand bottom; Station 179, depth 488 fathoms, mud bottom; Station 187, depth 13 fathoms, muddy sand bottom.

The species was described from the Timms Point Formation (Pleistocene) of southern California and also occurs in modern bays at Santa Catalina Island (LeRoy, 1943, p. 358).

NUMBER OF SPECIMENS STUDIED: 25 +

Bairdia bradyi van den Bold
(Pl. 7, fig. 4)

Not *Bairdia foveolata* BOSQUET, 1852, Acad. Roy. Sci. Lettres, Beaux-Arts Belgique Mém. Couronnéc, v. 24, p. 21, Pl. 1, fig. 5 (= *Cuneocythere (Monsmirabilia) f.* by Keij, 1957)

Bairdia foveolata BRADY, 1868a, Fonds de la Mer, v. 1, p. 56, Pl. 7, figs. 4–6; 1880, Challenger Reports, p. 55, Pd. 8, figs. 1a–f; 2a–j
Bairdia subdeltoidea (Münster) (part). JONES, 1890, Supp. Mon. Cretaceous Entomostraca, p. 7
Bairdia bradyi VAN DEN BOLD, 1957, Micropaleontology, v. 3, p. 236, Pl. 1, fig. 5

Shell subtriangular-subtrapezoidal in side view, highest medially; dorsal margin strongly convex and umbonate in left valve, truncate-convex in right valve; ventral margin gently convex in left valve to slightly concave medially in right valve; anterior margin rounded and extended ventral to midheight in left valve, angulated and extended medially, truncate to slightly concave above in right valve; posterior margin strongly and acuminately extended medially, concave above. Valves moderately to strongly convex, greatest convexity median. Left valve larger than right, extending strongly beyond right along umbonate dorsum. Surface densely and finely punctate.

Hinge margin of right valve bears a narrow groove into which fits a ridge in edge of left valve; inner lamellae narrow, somewhat broader anteriorly than elsewhere; line of concrescence and inner margin separated terminally; radial canals short, numerous, and closely spaced, apparently with funnel-shaped terminations. Muscle scar a median group of five spots in which there are two pair side by side and a fifth spot dorsal to group.

Above features seen only in an immature right valve; outline of left valve based on Brady's 1880 illustrations.

Length of figured right valve 0.54 mm, height 0.28 mm, convexity 0.13 mm.

RELATIONSHIPS: The umbonate dorsum, strongly acuminate posterior end, and dense punctation in addition to general shape, hingement, and musculature are characteristic of this species. *B. subdeltoidea* Münster (1830, p. 64) is similar in shape but has a sparsely pustulose to smooth surface.

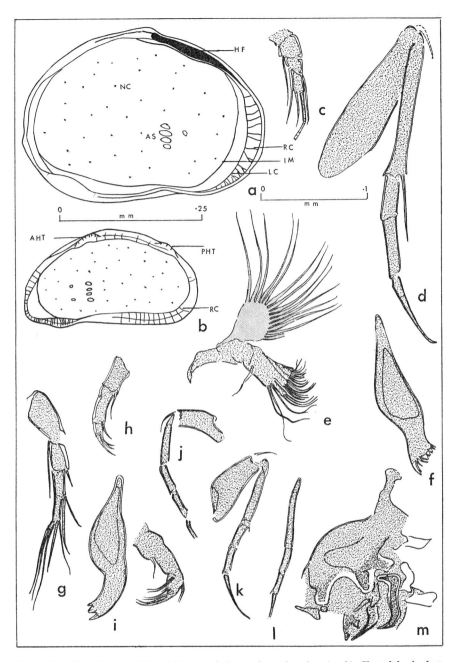

Figure 33. Xestoleberis, Sclerochilus, *and* Leguminocythereis. (a, b) *Xestoleberis hopkinsi* Skogsberg, Gulf of California, Station 102, interiors of female right valve and male left valve; (c–f) *Sclerochilus nasus* Benson, Scammon Lagoon, Baja California; (c) Antenna (incomplete); (d) First? thoracic leg; (e) Maxilla and respiratory lobe; (f) Mandible (coxa); (g–m) *?Leguminocythereis corrugata* LeRoy, Scammon Lagoon, Baja California; (g) Antennule; (h) Antenna (incomplete); (i) Mandible and palp; (j) First thoracic leg (incomplete); (k) Second thoracic leg; (l) Third thoracic leg (incomplete); (m) penis

37

OCCURRENCE: Recent, Gulf of California, Station 41, depth 45 fathoms, sand bottom. The species (B. "foveolata" of Brady) has been found in both the Atlantic and Pacific Oceans (Brady, 1880, p. 55).

NUMBER OF SPECIMENS STUDIED: 2

Bairdia cf. fortificata Brady, 1880
(Pl. 7, fig. 5)

Bairdia fortificata BRADY, 1880, Challenger Reports, Ostracoda, v. 1, p. 59, Pl. 11, figs. 4a, b; SWAIN 1952, U. S. Geol. Survey Prof. Paper 234-A, p. 16, Pl. 1, fig. 14

Shell subquadrate, dorsal and ventral margins nearly straight and subparallel; anterior margin rounded, extended medially, truncate above, finely spinose below; posterior margin more narrowly curved, extended and finely spinose below; truncate above; valves strongly convex, greatest convexity posterior and ventral to midheight. Surface densely and finely pitted. Left valve larger than right.

Hinge margin of left valve developed as a slight ridge that fits into corresponding groove in right valve. Inner lamellae of moderate width, broadest anteriorly; line of concrescence and inner margin separated terminally; radial canals poorly preserved or absent in present material; muscle scar an anteromedian group of five or six spots with no special pattern of arrangement.

Length of figured left valve 0.53 mm, height 0.26 mm, convexity of valve 0.15 mm.

REMARKS: The flattened dorsum, densely punctate surface, and spinose ends are diagnostic features of this species.

OCCURRENCE: Recent, Gulf of California, Station 41, depth 45 fathoms, sand bottom; Station 192, depth 262 fathoms, mud bottom. The species was described from the South Pacific. It also has been recorded from the Upper Miocene of North Carolina.

NUMBER OF SPECIMENS STUDIED: 25 +

Genus Bythocypris Brady, 1880

Bythocypris leroyi Swain nom. nov.
(Pl. 7, fig. 6)

Bythocypris elongata LEROY, 1943, Jour. Paleontology, v. 17, p. 358, Fig. 2a; Pl. 59, figs. 13–16; not Bythocypris elongata BRADY, 1880

Shell very thin, elongate, sublanceolate-subreniform in side view, highest medially; dorsal margin strongly convex, sloping more or less uniformly away from position of greatest height; ventral margin concave; anterior margin rounded, extended below; posterior margin much more narrowly curved, strongly extended below. Surface bears numerous irregularly spaced and irregularly sized shallow pits or impressions.

Hinge margin of left valve with narrow groove for reception of edge of right. Muscle scar a median group of about six spots.

Length of figured specimen 0.67 mm, height 0.36 mm, convexity of valve 0.16 mm.

REMARKS: The irregular outer surface of the valve was not mentioned in LeRoy's description of the species, but the outline of the present form seems identical to B. leroyi.

OCCURRENCE: Recent, Gulf of California, Station 179, depth 488 fathoms, mud bottom; originally described as rare in Lomita Marl "Pleistocene" of southern California.

NUMBER OF SPECIMENS STUDIED: 1

Superfamily CYPRIDACEA Baird, 1845
Family CYPRIDIDAE Baird, 1845
Subfamily CYPRIDINAE Baird, 1845
Genus Cyprinotus Brady, 1866

Cyprinotus unispinifera Furtos
(Fig. 34; Pl. 1, fig. 4; Pl. 4, figs. 1a, b)

Cyprinotus unispinifera FURTOS, 1936, Carnegie Inst. Washington Pub. 457, p. 106, Figs. 86–93

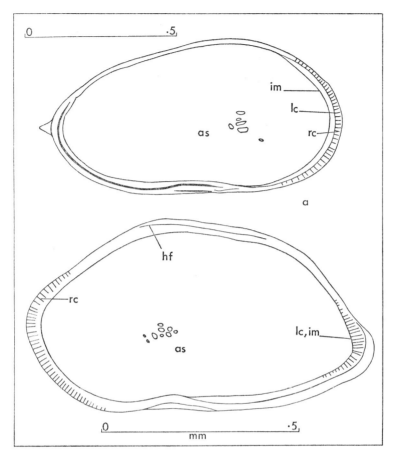

Figure 34. Cyprinotus *and* Bairdia. (a) *Cyprinotus unispinifera* Furtos, Gulf of California, Curray's Locality C–83, interior of left valve; (b) *Bairdia verdesensis* LeRoy, Gulf of California, Station 67, interior of right valve

The principal shell features of the species are as described for the genus. Subovate to subtriangular in side view, highest about two-fifths from anterior end; dorsal margin strongly convex with steeper anterior than posterior slope; ventral margin nearly straight to slightly concave medially; anterior margin broadly and nearly uniformly curved; posterior margin narrowly curved, strongly extended, and with a small spinose extension medially in left valve, less strongly extended and without spine in right valve. Left valve slightly larger than right; valves moderately convex, greatest convexity posteromedian. Surface smooth; free margins, especially the anterior, bear a narrow flangelike extension.

Hinge margin of left valve bears a long, narrow groove for reception of edge of right; inner lamellae very narrow; line of concrescence and inner margin separate; radial canals simple and evenly spaced anteriorly.

Length of holotype left valve 0.91 mm, height 0.45 mm, convexity of valve 0.27 mm.

RELATIONSHIPS: In general characteristics of the shell and posterior spine on one valve this species is similar to *Strandesia centrura* (Klie, 1940, p. 201) from Brazil; but that species is more elongate and has the posterior spine on the right, rather than the left, valve.

OCCURRENCE: Deltaic areas along eastern side of Gulf of California; common at Curray's

Station C-83, at kilometer 11.5 along road from Esquinapa to Las Cabras, Sinaloa, Mexico; in narrow lagoon between well-developed cheniers; surface of water covered with algal slime; salinity 91.2‰.

NUMBER OF SPECIMENS STUDIED: 100 +

Genus *Stenocypria* Müller, 1901

Stenocypria australia Swain sp. nov.
(Fig. 35; Pl. 1, fig. 10; Pl. 4, fig. 3 a–c)

Shell subelliptical-elongate in side view, highest anteromedially; dorsal margin gently convex, sloping slightly more steeply in front of than behind position of greatest height; ventral margin slightly concave medially, nearly straight overall; anterior margin broadly and nearly uniformly curved; posterior margin more narrowly curved, slightly extended below. Valves subequal, not strongly convex, greatest convexity anteromedian in position. Surface smooth. Anterior marginal zone compressed and somewhat extended flangelike.

Hingement consists of simple groove in left valve into which fits edge of right valve. Muscle scar a median group of five or six spots and two additional spots anteroventral to the main group. Inner lamellae broad and sinusoidal anteriorly and anteroventrally, less broad midventrally and posteriorly; line of concrescence and inner margin separate; radial canals few, irregular, and widely spaced.

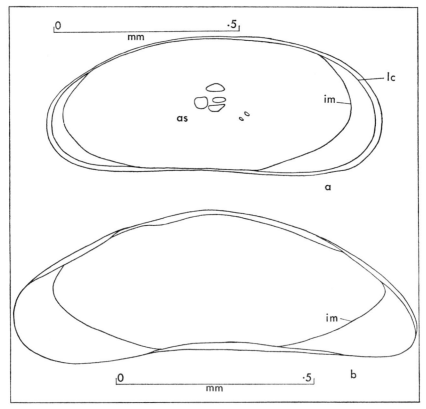

Figure 35. Stenocypria *and* Macrocyprina. (a) *Stenocypria australia* Swain sp. nov., Gulf of California, Curray's locality C-83; interior of left valve; (b) *Macrocyprina pacifica* (LeRoy), Gulf of California, Station 143

Length of holotype shell 0.87 mm, height 0.38 mm, convexity 0.27 mm.

RELATIONSHIPS: The new species is similar to *S. fischeri* Lilljeborg, 1883, in general shape and other shell features but is less elongate and has broader terminal margins than does *S. fischeri*.

OCCURRENCE: Restricted to deltaic areas along eastern margin of Gulf of California. The holotype is from Curray's Station C-80, edge of lagoon near road from Esquinapa to La Cabras, 13 km from Esquinapa, Sinaloa, Mexico; salinity 42‰.

NUMBER OF SPECIMENS STUDIED: 100 +

Subfamily CYPRIDOPSINAE

Genus *Potamocypris* Brady, 1870

Potamocypris mazatlanensis Swain sp. nov.

(Fig. 36; Pl. 1, figs. 3a, b; 5a, b)

Shell subtriangular to subtrapezoidal in side view, highest anterior to midlength; dorsal margin moderately convex, subangulate at position of greatest height, with short straightened anterior and longer straightened posterior slope; ventral margin concave medially to nearly straight; anterior margin broadly rounded; posterior margin narrowly rounded to subacuminate, extended below. Right valve larger than left, valves compressed, greatest convexity median. Surface minutely pitted and, in addition, with a very faint, coarsely reticulate pattern of ridges.

Hinge consists of simple narrow groove in edge of right valve into which fits edge of left valve. Inner lamellae very narrow anteriorly, almost absent elsewhere, slight vestibule; radical canals number about 15 anteriorly.

Length of holotype 0.53 mm, height 0.30 mm, convexity 0.21 mm.

RELATIONSHIPS: The general shape, right valve overlap, surface ornamentation, and

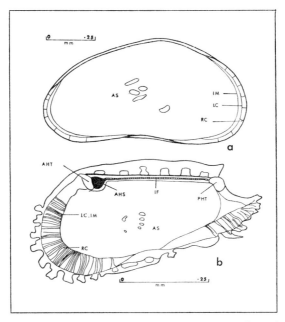

Figure 36. Potamocypris *and* Cativella. (a) *Potamocypris mazatlanensis* Swain sp. nov., Gulf of California, Curray's locality C-83, interior of left valve; (b) *Cativella dispar* Hartmann, Gulf of California, Station 123, interior of right valve

internal structure of the shell are like *Potamocypris*. The lack of strong projection of the right valve beyond the left middorsally is the distinguishing feature of the species together with the combined fine pitting and coarse reticulation of the surface. *P. isla-grandensis* Hartmann (1959a, p. 280) is about the same size as the present species, but its shell is less pointed posteriorly.

OCCURRENCE: Mouth of Presidio River near Mazatlan, Mexico, Curray's Station 83; at kilometer 11.5 along road from Esquinapa to Las Cabras, Sinaloa, Mexico, in narrow lagoon between well-developed cheniers; surface of water covered with algal slime; salinity 91.2‰.

NUMBER OF SPECIMENS STUDIED: 100 +

Family PARACYPRIDIDAE Sars, 1923
Genus *Macrocyprina* Triebel, 1960

Macrocyprina pacifica (LeRoy)
(Fig. 35, 37, 38b–g; Pl. 1, fig. 12)

Paracypris pacifica LEROY, 1943, Jour. Paleontology, v. 17, p. 358, Fig. 2z; Pl. 61, figs. 15–18

Paracypris pacifica LeRoy. BENSON, 1959 Kansas Univ. Paleont. Contr. Arthropoda, art. 1, p. 40, Pl. 1, fig. 4, Pl. 8, figs. 17

Diagnostic features of the shell of this species are: lateral outline of valves elongate lanceolate-reniform; dorsal margin moderately convex; ventral margin gently concave; terminal margins narrowly rounded, the posterior slightly more pointed than the anterior; valves compressed, surface smooth. Right valve larger than left, extending beyond edge of left along free margins, but along hinge left valve overlaps right. At ends of hinge margin of left valve are small weakly crenulate flanges. Inner lamellae broad ventroterminally, surface of lamellae with weak concentric circles.

The appendages are described here for the first time.

Antennule with terminal four segments progressively shorter and narrower; penultimate and third penultimate segments with four and two distal setae respectively; distal podomere bears five long terminal setae.

Antenna six-segmented, first three podomeres much longer than other; second podomere bears four proximal and four distal posterior setae, the proximal ones hollow part way down and terminate in long whiplash hairs; terminal three podomeres with numerous long distal setae.

Protopod of maxilla with three narrow, extended masticatory lobes; each with four clawlike setae; endopod palp has basal lamella three-segmented, but segments fused; first segment with one anterior distal seta, next segment with two setae, and third segment with six terminal setae, fourth segment of palp elongate, two-jointed with six to eight spines on ultimate joint and two spines on proximal joint.

First thoracic leg of female with long terminal spines and two adjacent shorter spines, penultimate joint with a single distal spine. Second leg has two strong, curved terminal spines. Third leg has a very long whiplike terminal spine that narrows and becomes ciliate in distal half.

Furca extended as a tweezerslike process, each limb of tweezers ciliate.

Length of figured right valve specimen 0.99 mm, height 0.41 mm, convexity of valve 0.15 mm.

OCCURRENCE: In the present collection, Gulf of California, Station 143, depth 10 fathoms, sand bottom; Station 175, depth 45 feet, sand bottom. It previously was recorded from "Pleistocene" Timms Point formation near Los Angeles, from modern environments near San Diego, California, and Ensenada, Mexico, both living and in sediments.

NUMBER OF SPECIMENS STUDIED: 10 (3 living)

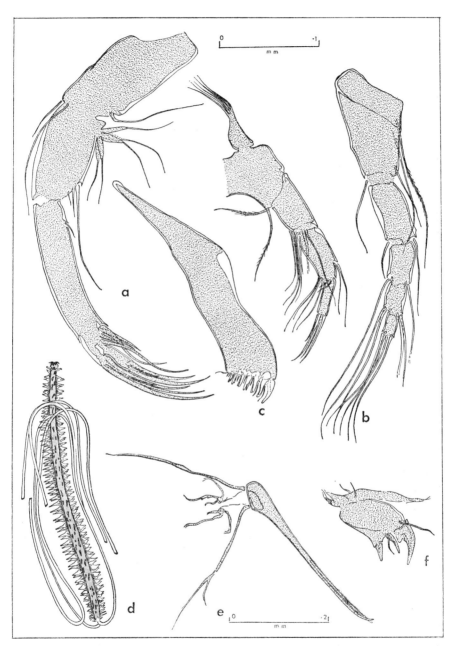

Figure 37. Macrocyprina pacifica *(LeRoy)*, *Scammon Lagoon, Baja California.* (a) Antenna; (b) Antennule; (c) Mandible and palp; (d) Ejaculatory apparatus; (e) Furca; (f) First thoracic leg, male

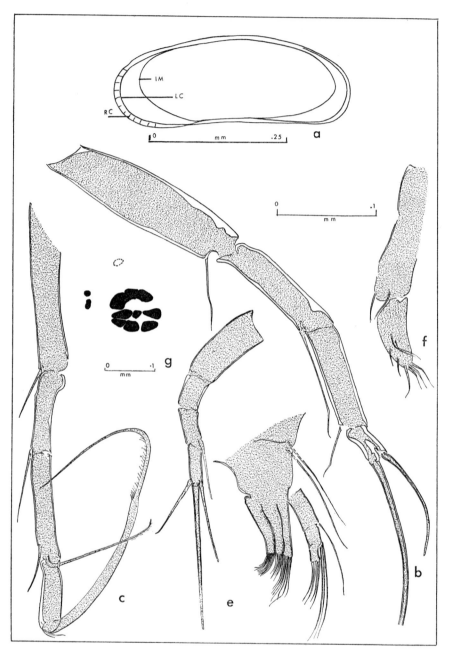

Figure 38. Aglaiocypris *and* Macrocyprina. (a) *Aglaiocypris virgenensis* Swain sp. nov., Gulf of California, Station 102, interior of left valve; (b–g) *Macrocyprina pacifica* (LeRoy), Scammon Lagoon, Baja California; (b) Second thoracic leg; (c) Third thoracic leg; (d) Maxilla; (e) Maxilliped female (first thoracic leg); (f) Palp of Maxilliped; (g) Adductor muscle scar

Genus *Paracypris* Sars, 1866

Paracypris franquesoides Swain sp. nov.
(Pl. 7, fig. 7)

Shell elongate lanceolate-subreniform in side view, highest about one-fourth from anterior end; dorsal margin strongly convex, sloping more steeply anterior to, than posterior to, position of greatest height; posterodorsal slope slightly truncate; ventral margin somewhat sinuous, concave anteromedially; anterior margin broadly curved; posterior margin acuminate, very strongly extended below. Valves subequal, the left slightly the larger, but right valve overlaps left along hinge; convexity of valves low, greatest convexity slightly anteromedian. Surface minutely pitted and finely hairy.

Hinge margin of right valve rabbeted for reception of edge of overlapped left valve. Inner lamellae very narrow in specimen at hand. Muscle scar lies at midlength and consists of several elongate scars lying in a circlet.

Length of figured specimen, probably an immature shell 0.75 mm, height 0.32 mm, convexity 0.22 mm.

RELATIONSHIPS: The greatly extended and acuminate posterior end, and weakly truncate posterodorsal slope of the present form relate it to *Paracypris franquesi* Howe and Chambers (1935, p. 10) from the Upper Eocene of Louisiana. That form, however, is considerably larger than the Gulf of California specimens.

OCCURRENCE: Recent, Gulf of California, Station 41, depth 45 fathoms, sand bottom; Station 179, depth 488 fathoms, mud bottom.

NUMBER OF SPECIMENS STUDIED: 2

Paracypris politella Swain sp. nov.
(Pl. 7, figs. 8a–c)

Shell elongate-lanceolate-subreniform in lateral view, highest about one-third from anterior end; dorsal margin moderately convex, with truncated slope posterior to position of greatest height; ventral margin concave; anterior margin broadly curved; posterior margin very narrowly curved to subacuminate, strongly extended below. Left valve slightly larger than right. Valves more or less compressed, greatest convexity median. Surface smooth.

Hinge margin of left valve bears a weak narrow groove for reception of edge of right valve; inner lamellae broad terminally, narrower ventrally, line of concrescence and inner margin widely separated. Radial canals very short, not numerous or closely spaced. Muscle scar consists of a median compact group of about four spots.

Length of figured left valve 0.81 mm, height 0.37 mm, convexity 0.17 mm.

RELATIONSHIPS: The outline and internal shell features of the Gulf of California specimens relate them to *P. polita* Sars, but they are somewhat less elongate and smaller than is typical of the Atlantic examples, and are here referred to a new species.

OCCURRENCE: Recent, Gulf of California, Station 175, depth 7.5 fathoms, sand bottom.

NUMBER OF SPECIMENS STUDIED: 2

Genus *Aglaiocypris* Sylvester-Bradley, 1946

Aglaiocypris virgenensis Swain sp. nov.
(Fig. 38; Pl. 4, fig. 4)

Shell elongate, elliptical-subreniform in side view, highest medially to posteromedially, dorsal margin gently convex; ventral margin slightly concave; terminal margins rounded, the anterior slightly narrower and more extended below than posterior. Valves compressed, greatest convexity median. Surface smooth.

Hingement consists of simple overlap of right valve by left. Inner lamellae of moderate width with inner margin and line of concrescence well separated terminally; radial canals few and rather widely spaced; adductor muscle scar a medially placed group of three or four crescent-shaped spots, arranged longitudinally, and with another rounded spot posterior to main group.

Length of holotype 0.43 mm, height 0.19 mm, convexity 0.08 mm.

RELATIONSHIPS: The elongate equal-ended shell and features of hingement, muscle scar, and inner lamellae furnish a relationship to *Aglaiocypris*. The species is similar in general form to *A. complanata* Brady and Robertson (1869, p. 365) from the Mediterranean and Atlantic regions but is more elongate.

OCCURRENCE: Rare in Gulf of California, Station 197, depth 28 fathoms, sandy mud bottom.

NUMBER OF SPECIMENS STUDIED: 3

Family PONTOCYPRIDIDAE Müller, 1894
Genus *Argilloecia* Sars, 1866

Argilloecia sp.
(Pl. 7, figs. 9a–d)

Shell elongate, sublanceolate in side view, highest anteromedially; dorsal margin moderately and uniformly convex; ventral margin concave anteromedially; anterior margin broadly curved, slightly extended and angulate above; posterior margin subacuminate, strongly extended below; valves subequal, convexity low; greatest convexity posteromedian. Surface smooth.

Hinge surface of left valve with terminal slightly extended flanges and interterminal depressed valve margin. Inner lamellae very broad terminally, especially anteriorly; line of concrescence and inner margin widely separated; radial canals few, short, and widely spaced. Muscle scar lies slightly anterior and dorsal to middle; it consists of subcircular compact group of four spots.

Length of figured left valve (Pl. 7, fig. 9b) 0.48 mm, height 0.18 mm, convexity 0.07 mm.

REMARKS: The outline and internal structures of this form suggest that it is an *Argilloecia;* but only four left valves are at hand, and they cannot be definitely assigned to a species.

OCCURRENCE: Recent, Gulf of California, Station 179, depth 488 fathoms, mud bottom.

NUMBER OF SPECIMENS STUDIED: 4

Superfamily DARWINULACEA Brady and Norman, 1889
Family DARWINULIDAE Brady and Norman, 1889
Genus *Darwinula* Brady and Norman, 1885

Darwinula yaquensis Swain sp. nov.
(Pl. 4, figs. 2a, b)

Shell elongate-subelliptical in side view, highest about one-fifth from posterior end; dorsal margin straight, about three-fifths of length with a slightly more obtuse anterior than posterior marginal bend; ventral margin nearly straight to slightly concave medially; anterior margin rounded, slightly extended below; posterior margin more broadly rounded. Right valve a little larger than left. Valves compressed. Length 2½ times height. Surface smooth.

Hinge margin of right valve grooved to receive edge of left valve. Inner lamellae very narrow. Adductor muscle scar is located anteromedially, is rosette shaped, and consists of several spots.

Length of holotype right valve (Pl. 4, fig. 2a) 0.45 mm, height 0.18 mm, convexity 0.11 mm.

RELATIONSHIPS: The shape, overlap, and musculature of the species ally it to *Darwinula* Brady and Robertson. It is more blunt ended than *D. stevensoni* (Brady and Robertson 1872, p. 50) and has a more concave venter than most other species of the genus.

OCCURRENCE: Rare in eastern nearshore part of middle Gulf of California, Station 111, depth 7 fathoms, hard clay bottom. Named from Rio Yaqui, Sonora, Mexico.
NUMBER OF SPECIMENS STUDIED: 2

Superfamily CYTHERACEA Baird, 1850
Family BRACHYCYTHERIDAE Puri, 1954
Genus *Pterygocythereis* Blake, 1933

Pterygocythereis delicata (Coryell and Fields)
(Fig. 39; Pl. 3, figs. 3a, b 4a–c)

Navecythere delicata CORYELL AND FIELDS, 1937, Am. Mus. Nov., no. 956, p. 7, Figs. 7a–c
Trachyleberis semitranslucens CROUCH, 1949, Jour. Paleontology, v. 23, p. 598
Pterygocythereis semitranslucens (Crouch). BENSON, 1959, Kansas Univ. Paleont. Contr., Arthropoda, art. 1, p. 27, Pl. 10, figs. 10, 11?

Shell elongate, subpyriform-sublanceolate in side view, highest about one-third from anterior end; dorsal margin slightly convex, jagged owing to projecting spines that number about 12; ventral margin sinuous; dorsal and ventral margins converge toward posterior; anterior margin broadly curved, irregularly spinose, with about nine blunt spines; posterior margin acuminately extended at midheight, concave above, with one long and two short spines below. Valves subequal in size judged from proportion and selvage structure, left overlaps edge of right. Valves compressed, greatest convexity slightly posteromedian in position.

Dorsal and anterior marginal areas of adult shells bear numerous thick, short spines mentioned above; in immature molts these spines united at ends to form a perforated frill that extends along venter as well as along anterior and dorsal margins. In mature shells ventral border bears only a low ridge and a few spines as remnants of frill structure of instar valves. Surface also has a ventromedian strongly elevated longitudinal ridge or series of connected hollow nodes at posterior end of which is a high, long spine. General surface smooth.

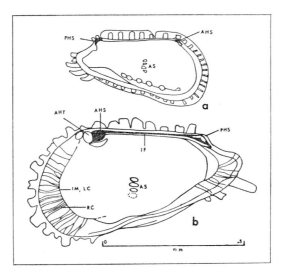

Figure 39. Pterygocythereis delicata *(Coryell and Fields), Gulf of California.* Interiors of (a) Immature left valve, Station 123, and (b) Mature right valve, Station 119

Hinge of right valve consists of an anterior high, bluntly pointed, somewhat curved tooth, posterojacent deep rounded socket, narrow shallow interterminal groove, and posterior curved tooth beneath which is a small triangular socket; hinge of left valve has corresponding anterior socket and tooth, interterminal bar, and posterior socket. Inner lamellae of medium width, line of concrescence and inner margin coincide; radial canals numerous, long, and closely spaced anteriorly, shorter and fewer ventrally and terminally. Muscle scar not observed.

Length of figured right valve (Pl. 3, fig. 3a) excluding terminal spines 0.75 mm, height 0.38 mm, convexity of valve excluding ventral high ridge and spine 0.15 mm.

REMARKS: In general shape, ventral alate ridge, spinose margins, and internal structures the species is similar to *Pterygocythereis jonesi* (Baird 1850, p. 175) of the North Atlantic region but is more acuminate posteriorly and has ventral ridge less strongly elevated. The specimens referred to by Crouch (1949, p. 598) as early instars of "*Trachyleberis*" *semitranslucens*, in which median ridge is not yet developed, are believed to represent instars of *P. delicata*.

OCCURRENCE: Recent, Gulf of California, Station 39, depth 21 fathoms, muddy sand bottom; Station 41, depth 45 fathoms, sand bottom; Station 52, depth 25 fathoms, sandy mud bottom; Station 77, depth 3 fathoms, sand bottom; Station 87, depth 7 fathoms, sandy mud bottom; Station 88, depth 8 fathoms, gravel and sand bottom; Station 24, depth 4 fathoms, sand bottom; Station 100, depth 38 fathoms, gravel and sand bottom; Station 102, depth 6 fathoms, sand bottom; Station 110, depth 10 fathoms, sand bottom; Station 111, depth 7 fathoms, hard clay bottom; Station 112, depth 34 fathoms, hard clay bottom; Station 119, depth 31 fathoms, sand bottom; Station 123, depth 5 fathoms, sandy mud bottom; Station 138, depth 17 fathoms, muddy sand bottom; Station 141, depth 10 fathoms, sand bottom; Station 144, depth 75 fathoms, sandy mud bottom; Station 153, depth 18 fathoms, muddy sand bottom; Station 155, depth 15 fathoms, muddy sand bottom; Station 158, depth 17 fathoms, muddy sand bottom; Station 180, depth 14 fathoms, sand bottom; Station 187, depth 13 fathoms, muddy sand bottom; Station 194, depth 75 fathoms, muddy sand bottom; Station 201, depth 13 fathoms, muddy sand bottom; Station 204, depth 40 fathoms, muddy sand bottom; Station 216, depth 18 fathoms, sandy mud bottom; and Station 217, depth 15 fathoms, sandy mud bottom. Reported by Crouch from Recent of Cristobal Bay, Baja California, and by Benson in Todos Santos Bay, Sonora, Mexico. The species was described from the Gatun Formation, Miocene, of Panama.

NUMBER OF SPECIMENS STUDIED: 25 +

Pterygocythereis? cuevasensis Swain sp. nov.
(Pl. 8, fig. 7)

Shell sublanceolate in side view, highest anteromedially except for posteroventral alate extension; dorsal margin very long, nearly straight except for slight anteromedian sinuosity, anterior cardinal angle slightly obtuse, posterior cardinal angle acute; ventral margin convex but markedly sinuous posteromedially owing to alate extensions of valves, converging toward dorsum, posteriorly; anterior margin broadly curved, fringed with seven or more blunt spines; posterior margin pointed, strongly extended above, bearing small spines below. Valve compressed; greatest convexity is posteromidventral in alate expansion of shell.

Dorsal margin with narrow rim; ventral surface strongly expanded as a great bispinose ala, each spine is flattened longitudinally and bears a spinelike point; both spines continue dorsally across valve surface nearly to dorsal margin as low ridges between which lies a shallow sulcus; ventral surface of ala ornamented by a narrow ridge yolking the two spines, together with several reticulate ridges on underside of spines.

Hinge of right valve formed by an anterior rounded high tooth, posterojacent rounded socket, interterminal very narrow groove that bears weak crenulae and posterior tiny socket and posterojacent weak tooth. Inner lamellae fairly broad anteriorly, narrower ventrally and posteriorly; line of concrescence and inner margin slightly separated anteriorly; radial canals numerous and closely spaced anteriorly, fewer posteriorly. Muscle scar formed of a small anteromedian subvertical row of four closely spaced spots; other spots not observed.

Length of holotype right valve 0.50 mm, height 0.23 mm, convexity of valve 0.17 mm.

RELATIONSHIPS: The general form of hingement, the shape and alation of this species are like *Pterygocythereis* Blake, but the sulcate midsection of the shell is more like *Monoceratina* Roth. At present the species will be referred questionably to *Pterygocythereis*.

OCCURRENCE: Recent, Gulf of California, Station 41, depth 45 fathoms, sand bottom. Species named for village of Las Cuevas, Baja California, near which collecting station is located.

NUMBER OF SPECIMENS STUDIED: 2

Family BYTHOCYTHERIDAE Sars, 1926
Genus *Miracythere* Hornibrook, 1952

Miracythere? sp.
(Pl. 9, fig. 12)

Shell subquadrate in side view, highest one-third from anterior end; dorsal margin nearly straight with obtuse cardinal angles, the anterior less well defined and more obtuse than posterior; ventral margin concave medially; anterior margin very broadly curved; posterior margin narrower, slightly extended, and with a few tiny spines below, subtruncate above. Valves subequal, convexity moderate, most convex posterior to midlength; terminal sixth of valve strongly compressed.

Free margins of valve with narrow, smoothly rounded rim; dorsomedian surface with shallow sulcus that extends from dorsum to below midheight; valve surface anterior and posterior to sulcus forms two lobes, the posterior the more strongly elevated; ventromedian surface connecting the two lobes strongly swollen, slightly overhangs ventral margin medially; general surface, except flattened marginal areas finely and densely pitted; a few irregular narrow ridges occur on posterior lobe; a few pustules lie on posteroventral flattened area.

Hinge of left valve consists of terminal elongate teeth and an interterminal narrow weak groove; inner lamellae rather broad; line of concrescence and inner margin appear to be separated anteroventrally and posteriorly; radial canals not observed. Muscle scar lies in a small area near ventral end of median sulcus, but details were not observed.

Length of figured left valve 0.37 mm, height 0.23 mm, convexity 0.10 mm.

REMARKS: This form, probably immature, is related to *Miracythere* Hornibrook from New Zealand in general shape, lobation, and hingement. It may represent a new genus as it lacks the anterodorsal strong elevation of the shell of *Miracythere*, but only a single imperfect left valve is available for study.

OCCURRENCE: Recent, Gulf of California, Station 25, depth 1,655 fathoms, mud bottom; only empty shell found.

NUMBER OF SPECIMENS STUDIED: 1

Genus *Monoceratina* Roth, 1928

Monoceratina bifurcata Puri
(Pl. 7, figs. 13a, b)

Monoceratina bifurcata PURI, 1954 Florida Geol. Survey Bull. 36, p. 295, Figs. 12k–m; Pl. 15, figs. 6–10

Shell subquadrate-rhomboidal in side view, highest medially to anteromedially; dorsal margin gently convex, slightly sinuous, concave posteriorly; ventral margin moderately convex, somewhat sinuous medially due to overhang of midventral valve surface, converging toward posterior with dorsum; anterior margin broadly curved, extended medially to ventromedially; posterior margin narrower in curvature, strongly extended above, subtruncate dorsal and ventral to position of greatest extension. Valves subequal, strongly convex in ventral part of shell.

Dorsal marginal zone with high narrow ridge; a subvertical short ridge extends ventrally from dorsal ridge near anterior end of hinge line; midventral half of shell strongly expanded as a low alaform ridge that curves dorsally and terminates at midheight; broad median sulcus defined by alaform ridge and short anterodorsal ridge; a short ridgelike spur extends from anteroventral side of ventral ala; ventral surface of ala has rows of pits arranged in narrow grooves; general surface bears small pits; anterior margin with narrow rim.

Hinge of right valve consists of a narrow long groove, slightly broadened at ends into which fits a corresponding ridge of left valve; *i.e.*, a crude "lophodont" type of hinge; inner lamellae of moderate width ventroterminally, becoming narrower above midheight; radial canals few and widely spaced anteriorly, longer and sinuous posteriorly; line of concrescence and inner margin separate terminally. Adductor muscle scar lies at ventral end of median sulcus and consists of an oblique subvertical row of four more or less elongate spots in a small group.

Length of figured left valve 0.60 mm, height 0.37 mm, convexity of valve 0.23 mm.

REMARKS: This species is probably conspecific with *Monoceratina bifurcata* Puri from the Miocene of Florida, but the Miocene forms have lower and less sharp-crested surface ridges.

OCCURRENCE: Recent, Gulf of California, Station 41, depth 45 fathoms, sand bottom; Station 162, depth 13 fathoms, sand bottom; Station 179, depth 488 fathoms, mud bottom. It was recorded by Puri from the Chipola and Cancellaria facies of the Alum Bluff and Choctawhatchee stages, respectively, Middle and Upper Miocene, of Florida.

NUMBER OF SPECIMENS STUDIED: 3

Family CYTHERIDEIDAE Sars, 1925
Subfamily CYTHERIDEINAE Sars, 1925
Genus *Cyprideis* Jones, 1857

Cyprideis currayi Swain sp. nov.
(Pl. 7, figs. 11a–c, 12)

Shell elongate-subelliptical to subovate in side view, highest medially; dorsal margin gently convex; ventral margin slightly concave; anterior margin broadly curved, slightly extended below; posterior margin slightly narrower, subtruncate medially. Left valve a little larger than right, extending beyond it anteriorly. Valves moderately convex; greatest convexity posterior in position.

Valve margins with narrow, slightly compressed and extended border anteriorly and ventroposteriorly; median valve surface vertically depressed as a broad sulcus, and a narrow, oblique furrow occurs anterodorsally; general surface coarsely and deeply pitted in middle part, more finely pitted in marginal areas.

Hinge margin of right valve consists of an anterior elongate weakly crenulate ridge element, an interterminal crenulate furrow, and a posterior denticulate ridge element. Muscle scar consists of an anteromedian subvertical, slightly curved row of four spots anterior to which are two additional antennal spots, of which the dorsal is the larger. Inner lamellae rather narrow; line of concrescence and inner margin only slightly separated; radial canals numerous and closely spaced anteriorly, more widely spaced elsewhere.

Length of holotype right valve 0.73 mm, height 0.40 mm, convexity of valve 0.20 mm.

RELATIONSHIPS: The undifferentiated nature of the interterminal portion of the hinge allies this species with *Neocyprideis* Apostolescu, 1956. The coarsely pitted surface is similar to that of *Cyprideis rohri* van den Bold (1963, p. 378) from the Pliocene of Trinidad, but that species has the anteromedian furrow more strongly developed.

OCCURRENCE: Recent, in lake 70 m from bank behind a submerged chenier covered with mangroves; soft mud bottom with many shell fragments; water depth 75 cm, salinity 5.8‰; located about 1 km east of Mexcaltitan, Nayarit, Mexico; also from same lake 250 m N. 50° E. of preceding locality, water depth 50 cm, near clump of hyacinths with roots to bottom.

NUMBER OF SPECIMENS STUDIED: 25 +

Family CYTHERIDAE Baird, 1845
Subfamily PERISSOCYTHERIDEINAE van den Bold, 1963
Genus *Pumilocytheridea* van den Bold, 1963

Pumilocytheridea sp.
(Pl. 3, fig. 7)

Shell small, elongate subpyriform in side view, highest about one-third from anterior end; dorsal margin strongly convex, sloping more steeply in front of than behind position of greatest height; ventral margin slightly concave medially; anterior margin broadly curved, extended below; posterior margin narrowly rounded, subacuminately extended below. Valves subequal, not strongly convex, greatest convexity ventromedian.

Middorsal surface of valves with a narrow, vertical, groovelike sulcus that extends to midheight; a small median swelling lies anterior to ventral end of sulcus, and a narrow, low, longitudinal ridge extends posteriorly from lower ends of sulcus; a ventromedian long, low ridge most elevated posteriorly lies ventrad of sulcus; general surface minutely ornamented with an irregularly reticulate pattern of ridges and pits; short spurs extend from flanks of longitudinal ridges.

Hinge of right valve consists of terminal elongate crenulate teeth and an interterminal furrow. Inner lamellae not developed in specimen at hand. Muscle scar not observed.

Length of figured immature right valve 0.33 mm, height 0.17 mm, convexity 0.08 mm.

REMARKS: The outline, surface ornamentation, and hingement of this species are like *Pumilocytheridea* van den Bold. All the specimens at hand appear to be immature and cannot be placed specifically.

OCCURRENCE: Recent, Gulf of California, Station 67, depth 4 fathoms, sand bottom; Station 216, depth 18 fathoms, sandy mud bottom; Station 88, depth 8 fathoms, gravel and sand bottom; Station 153, depth 18 fathoms, muddy sand bottom; Station 158, depth 17 fathoms, muddy sand bottom; Station 187, depth 13 fathoms, muddy sand bottom; Station 192, depth 262 fathoms, mud bottom.

NUMBER OF SPECIMENS STUDIED: 7

Pumilocytheridea vermiculoidea Swain sp. nov.
(Fig. 40; Pl. 3, figs. 6a–d)

Shell elongate-sublanceolate in side view, highest about one-third from anterior end; dorsal margin slightly convex, sloping more steeply in front of, than behind, position of greatest height; ventral margin slightly concave to nearly straight; anterior margin broadly curved, extended below; posterior margin narrowly rounded, extended medially. Left valve slightly larger than right, overlapping along free margins, moderately convex, greatest convexity median.

General surface densely pitted; anterior end with submarginal narrow ridge from ventromedian side of which a ridge extends anteriorly and dorsally to about two-fifths of shell length where it doubles back nearly to join anterior ridge; a sinuous, subvertical anteromedian furrow extends from near dorsal margin, nearly to midheight where it joins a longitudinal furrow; posterodorsal shell surface with several short sublongitudinal narrow ridges and intervening narrow furrows. A small eye tubercle occurs anterodorsally, and a narrow sulcus extends obliquely to midheight from eye tubercle.

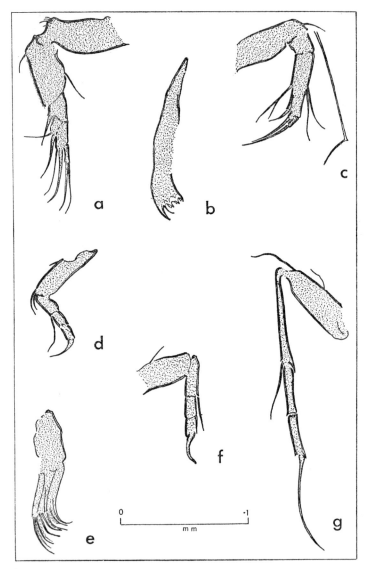

Figure 40. Pumilocytheridea vermiculoidea *Swain sp. nov., Gulf of California, Station 111.* (a) Antennule; (b) Mandible (coxa); (c) Antenna; (d) First thoracic leg; (e) Maxilla; (f) Second thoracic leg; (g) Third thoracic leg

Hinge surface of both valves deeply incised below outer margin in posterior half. Hinge of left valve consists of terminal grooves or elongate sockets, each of which bears a few low transverse ridges and an interterminal smooth bar; hinge of right valve consists of terminal elongate faintly crenulate bars and intervening groove. Inner lamellae relatively narrow; line of concrescence and inner margin separated terminally; radial canals few and widely spaced terminally; adductor muscle scar consists of an anteromedian subvertical row of four closely spaced spots, perhaps with one or more additional antennal spots anterior to main group.

Male shells more elongate than those of females.

Antennule with five podomeres; first and second sharply geniculate, about equal in length, distal outer margin of first with three small setae, second with several small outer and inner proximal setae and an outer distal seta; third and fourth podomeres about half length of second and narrower, tapering; fourth podomere represents fusion of two segments; third podomere with one outer distal clawlike seta; fourth podomere has four outer setae, two at approximate distal edge of proximal incipient segment and two at distal end of segment; fifth podomere very narrow and with one thick, clawlike spine and a thinner seta.

Antenna consists of four podomeres; exopodite long, extending beyond distal claws; second podomere much shorter than first; third podomere represents fusion of two segments; at distal end of incipient proximal podomere are two inner and two outer setae; at distal end of third podomere, an inner claw; fourth segment very small, with two strong terminal claws.

Masticatory edge of mandible with two longer outer teeth and three shorter inner teeth. Maxilla with three masticatory lobes, each of which is extended into a pair of stiff bristles.

First thoracic leg four-segmented; proximal segment with median outer, and one or two (varies from right to left leg) distal seta; second segment with outer distal seta; ultimate segment with curved terminal claw. Second thoracic leg similar, but a little larger. Third thoracic leg much longer, four-segmented, similar setae; terminal claw very long and curving.

Length of holotype male shell (Pl. 3, fig. 6b) 0.48 mm, height 0.20 mm, convexity 0.18 mm.

RELATIONSHIPS: The sublanceolate form, hingement, delicate surface ornamentation, and depressed posterodorsal valve margins ally this species with *Pumilocytheridea*. The pattern of surface ridges is somewhat similar to that in *P. sandbergi* van den Bold, the type species, but that form is more reticulate than the present species. The appendages of the genus are described here for the first time.

OCCURRENCE: Recent, frequent in Gulf of California, sediment at Station 189, depth 10 fathoms, sand bottom; rare at Station 102, depth 6 fathoms, sand bottom.

NUMBER OF SPECIMENS STUDIED: 6 (2 living)

Genus *Perissocytheridea* Stephenson, 1938

Perissocytheridea meyerabichi (Hartmann)
(Figs. 41f–i, 44c, d; Pl. 4, figs. 7a, b, 8a–c; Pl. 8, figs. 1a–d)

Iliocythere meyerabichi HARTMANN, 1953, Zool. Anz., v. 151, p. 310, Figs. 1–10; HARTMANN, 1957, Kieler Meeresforschungen, v. 13, p. 141
Perissocytheridea meyerabichi (Hartmann). BENSON AND KAESLER, 1963, Kansas Univ. Paleont. Contr., Arthropoda, art. 3, p. 17, Fig. 7; Pl. 4, figs. 1–5

Shell strongly dimorphic. *Male* shells subpyriform-trapezoidal in side view; dorsal margin straight to slightly sinuous, with anterior cardinal angle somewhat more obtuse than posterior; ventral margin sinuous, converging posteriorly toward dorsum; anterior margin broadly curved, slightly extended below, subtruncate above; posterior margin bluntly acuminate, extended slightly ventrad of midheight, strongly truncate to slightly concave above, subtruncate below. Left valve larger than right, extending beyond right most noticeably in cardinal areas and terminally. Valves moderately convex, greatest convexity posteromedian. *Female* shells shorter and higher, more subquadrate; ventral margin nearly straight to slightly concave medially.

Anterodorsal valve surface bears a shallow, narrow oblique sulcus that dies out about one-third from dorsal margin; a short subvertical anteromedian sulcus is evident in some specimens but is represented only by an internal corresponding ridge in other specimens; general surface marked by coarsely reticulate pattern of ridges, the interspaces between

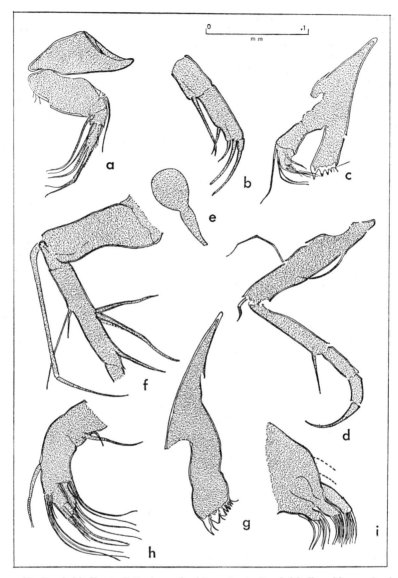

Figure 41. Parakrithella *and* Perissocytheridea. (a–e) *Parakrithella oblonga* Swain sp. nov., Gulf of California, Station 123; (a) Antennule; (b) Antenna (incomplete); (c) Mandible and palp; (d) Second thoracic leg; (e) Efferent duct of flagellum (or exopodite) of antenna; (f–i) *Perissocytheridea meyerabichi* (Hartmann), Gulf of California, Curray's Locality C-80; (f) Antenna (incomplete); (g) Mandible (coxa); (h) Palp of mandible; (i) Maxilla

which in some instances bear two or three pits; two slightly more prominent ridges trend irregularly backward from midshell; posteromidventral shell surface a little more elevated than surrounding area; posterior end of shell more or less compressed; dorsal and terminal margins bear narrow flangelike rim.

Hinge of right valve consists of terminal elongate toothlike elevations, each bearing five or six crenulae and an interterminal long, depressed, weakly crenulate groove, rabbeted below; hinge of left valve correspondingly consists of terminal crenulate sockets and intervening denticulate rabbet-bar. Inner lamellae narrow; line of concrescence and inner margin slightly separated anteriorly; radial canals few and widely spaced, occurring in groups of two or three.

Only a few appendages preserved in present specimens. Antenna of female with long second podomere formed by fusion of three segments, two anterior setae from distal end of first fused segment, two long posterior clawlike setae from what appears to be proximal end of second fused segment, and a posterior large seta from distal end of same segment; expodite long and two-jointed.

Mandible with six teeth; palp three-segmented, each portion bearing two or three claws.

Length of figured specimen (Pl. 8, fig. 1a) 0.62 mm, height 0.36 mm, convexity 0.28 mm.

REMARKS: The subpyriform to subquadrate shape, sulcation, and hingement ally this species with *Perissocytheridea*. The coarsely reticulate surface and posteromedian weak sinuous ridges are distinguishing features of the species.

OCCURRENCE: Recent, Gulf of California, Station 19, depth 8 fathoms, sand bottom; Station 39, depth 21 fathoms, muddy sand bottom; Station 197, depth 28 fathoms, sandy mud bottom; Station 216, depth 18 fathoms, sandy mud bottom.

J. E. Curray's localities, south of Mazatlan as follows: C-80, at edge of lagoon near road from Esquinapa to Las Cabras, Sinaloa, Mexico, at kilometer 13 from Esquinapa; salinity 42.0‰; farther to north salt is being precipitated from the lagoon water; C-83, at kilometer 11.5 along some road in narrow lagoon between well-developed cheniers; surface of water covered with an algal slime; salinity 91.2‰; C-112 about 1 km east of Mexcaltitan, Nayarit, Mexico, in lake 70 m from bank behind a submerged chenier covered with mangroves, soft mud bottom with many shell fragments; water depth 7.5 cm, salinity 5.8‰; C-113, same lake, 250 m to N. 50° E., water depth 50 cm, near clump of water hyacinths with roots to bottom; C-114, same lake, 250 m to N. 50° E., water depth 38 cm; C-115, same lake, 250 m farther on same course, about 50 m from other bank, which represents a submerged mangrove-covered chenier; water depth 35 cm; mud at least 7 m thick and very soft.

NUMBER OF SPECIMENS STUDIED: 100 + (1 living)

Subfamily KRITHINAE Mandelstam, 1958

Genus *Krithe* Brady, Crosskey, and Robertson, 1874

Krithe producta Brady

(Pl. 9, fig. 1)

Krithe producta BRADY, 1880, *Challenger* Reports, Ostracoda, p. 114, Pl. 27, figs. 1a–g; BRADY AND NORMAN, 1889, Roy. Dublin Soc. Trans., v. 4, ser. 2, p. 180, Pl. 17, figs. 5–7; EGGER, 1901, Köngl. Bayerischen Akad. Wiss. Abh. Math.-phys. Kl., v. 21, p. 451, Pl. 4, figs. 17, 18

Shell subovate in side view, highest medially; dorsal margin moderately convex, merging gradually with anterior margin but bending abruptly into posterior margin; ventral margin nearly straight, forming abrupt angulation with posterior margin but merging gradually with anterior margin; anterior margin broadly and uniformly curved; posterior margin narrowly curved and strongly extended below, truncate above, slightly produced beyond valve margin. Valves moderately convex, greatest convexity slightly posteromedian; valves subequal, general surface of valve smooth and shiny; normal canals prominent and widely spaced, marked by small pits around which is a clear circlet.

Hinge of left valve consists of a ridge in anterior half, a depressed posteromedian segment, dorsal to which is narrow accommodation groove, and an elongate posterior toothlike elevation. Hinge of right valve not seen but presumably the antithesis of left. Inner lamellae rather narrow, broadest anteriorly, line of concrescence and inner margin separated anteriorly; radial canals not clearly seen but apparently are numerous and closely spaced anteriorly. Adductor muscle scar a median subvertical row of four separated spots and a more-anterior trilobate spot. Midventral margin of left with prominent asymmetrical selvage apophysis and ventral selvage furrow.

Length of figured left valve 0.72 mm, height 0.40 mm, convexity of valve 0.20 mm.

REMARKS: The shape, smooth surface, hingement, musculature, and marginal structures allies this species with *Krithe* Brady, Crosskey, and Robertson; and the produced posteroventral margin relates it to *K. producta* Brady (1880, Pl. 27, fig. 1a).

OCCURRENCE: Recent, Gulf of California, Station 60, depth 1480 fathoms, mud bottom; Station 179, depth 488 fathoms, mud bottom; Station 192, depth 262 fathoms, mud bottom. The species is widely distributed in the Atlantic Ocean, Indian Ocean, and South Pacific. The present occurrence is apparently the first in the eastern Pacific.

NUMBER OF SPECIMENS STUDIED: 5

Genus *Parakrithe* van den Bold, 1958

Parakrithe? sp.
(Pl. 9, figs. 2a, b)

Two immature specimens in the present collection have the following characteristics: lateral outline subelliptical, highest medially; dorsal margin slightly convex, truncated anteriorly; ventral margin slightly concave medially; anterior margin broadly curved, extended slightly above, subtruncate below; posterior margin more narrowly curved. Valves subequal, the left slightly larger than right; valves of medium convexity, greatest convexity posteromedian. Surface smooth.

Hinge surface of right valve consists of a weak rabbet groove in anterior two-thirds, behind which hinge margin is weakly denticulate. Inner lamellae narrow in immature shells at hand; vestibule narrow terminally, not deeply reentrant as in *Krithe*; radial canals fairly numerous but short. Adductor muscle scar consists of a median vertical row of four elongate spots and two additional more-anterior spots, the more dorsal of which is C-shaped.

Length of figured right valve 0.43 mm, height 0.20 mm, convexity of valve 0.10 mm.

REMARKS: The narrow inner lamellae and hingement of these specimens suggest *Parakrithe* van den Bold, although this may be due to lack of development of the sinuous line of concrescence found in *Krithe*, in the present immature forms. No specific assignment is attempted with the present material.

OCCURRENCE: Recent, Gulf of California, Station 204, depth 40 fathoms, muddy sand bottom.

NUMBER OF SPECIMENS STUDIED: 2

Genus *Parakrithella* Hanai, 1961

Parakrithella oblonga Swain sp. nov.
(Fig. 41a–e; Pl. 9, figs. 3a–c)

Shell elongate-subovate to subelliptical in side view, highest about one-third from posterior end; dorsal margin convex, sloping gently anterior to, more steeply posterior to position of greatest height; ventral margin slightly concave anteromedially; anterior margin broadly curved; posterior margin more narrowly curved, extended medially. Valves subequal, the left slightly larger than and extending beyond right valve along free margins. Valves moderately convex, greatest convexity posteromedian. Surface smooth.

Hinge margin of left valve formed of slightly recessed valve edge that receives the slightly extended edge of left valve. Inner lamellae broad; line of concrescence and inner margin widely separated; line of concrescence forming a crescentic reentrant anteriorly; radial canals number about 15 anteriorly, more closely spaced below than in dorsal half, with funnel-shaped inner terminations that produce a scalloped outline along line of concrescence. Muscle scar an anteromedian vertical row of four elongate closely spaced spots and two additional more-anterior spots, of which the dorsal spot is much the larger.

Antennule with very broad first and second podomeres; third podomere very short; fourth longer and more geniculate than third; fifth short and rounded; second podomere with many small anterior hairs, fourth with one or two anterior setae; and fifth with anterior setae as well as five long terminal swimming claws.

Antenna two-segmented; second segment consists of about three fused segments and bears four strong claws, three distal and one posterior near distal end; exopodite not reaching beyond distal end of appendage, excluding claws.

Mandible with five teeth and a seta from edge of mandible near anterior side; palp three-segmented, with four or five terminal claws.

Thoracic legs four-segmented; proximal one represents fusion of two and with a posterior proximal seta, an anterior seta at junction of fused segments, and a larger, thicker seta at distal end; second long podomere with anterior distal seta; third and fourth podomeres half length of second; terminal claw strongly curved.

Length of holotype shell 0.53 mm, height 0.27 mm, convexity 0.22 mm.

RELATIONSHIPS: The general shape and some of the internal structures of this species relate it to *Paradoxostoma rarum* Müller (1894, p. 320) from the Bay of Naples. In that species, however, the zone of concrescence is narrower, and the shell is less convex than in the present specimens. The generic assignment of this species is somewhat uncertain; but the marginal features, hingement, and musculature relate it more nearly to *Parakrithella* than to *Paradoxostoma*. Furthermore, the antennules of the present form are shorter and broader, and the antennae are differently shaped than in the *Paradoxostoma*.

OCCURRENCE: Recent, Gulf of California, Station 123, depth 5 fathoms, sandy mud bottom.

NUMBER OF SPECIMENS STUDIED: 4 (1 living)

Subfamily NEOCYTHERIDEINAE Puri, 1957
Genus *Cushmanidea* Blake, 1933

Cushmanidea pauciradialis Swain sp. nov.
(Pl. 8, figs. 5a–c, 6a, b)

Shell elongate, sublanceolate-subreniform in side view, highest slightly posterior to midlength; dorsal margin moderately convex; ventral margin concave; anterior margin rounded, extended below and eight to ten small spines or serrations below; posterior margin narrowly curved, extended below, truncate above. Valves subequal, left slightly larger than right. Valve surface with shallow indistinct anteromedian sulcus in dorsal half; general surface smooth except for scattered pits that represent openings of normal pore canals.

Hinge of right valve consists of terminal elongate flanges and intervening furrow which correspond to terminal grooves and interterminal bar in left valve. Adductor muscle scar consists of an anteromedian slightly crescentic subvertical row of four closely spaced elongate spots and two additional more-anterior antennal spots. Inner lamellae broad anteriorly, narrower posteriorly and ventrally; line of concrescence and inner margin widely separated terminally; line of concrescence strongly scalloped anteriorly due to funnel-shaped inner termination of radial canals. Radial canals relatively few and widely spaced.

Length of holotype shell 0.65 mm, height 0.28 mm, convexity 0.26 mm.

RELATIONSHIPS: This species is similar to *C. elongata* (Brady 1868b, p. 421) from the Atlantic and Gulf of Mexico regions but has fewer radial canals, is weakly sulcate, and has the line of concrescence markedly scalloped anteriorly.

OCCURRENCE: Recent, Gulf of California, Station 41, depth 45 fathoms, sand bottom; Station 52, depth 25 fathoms, sandy mud bottom; Station 77, depth 3 fathoms, sand bottom; Station 88, depth 8 fathoms, gravel and sand bottom; Station 110, depth 10 fathoms, sand bottom; Station 140, depth 15 fathoms, shell and sand bottom; Station 147, depth 6 fathoms, sand bottom; Station 162, depth 13 fathoms, sand bottom; Station 175, depth 7.5 fathoms, sand bottom.

NUMBER OF SPECIMENS STUDIED: 25 +

Cushmanidea guardensis Swain sp. nov.
(Fig. 42; Pl. 8, figs. 4a–c)

Shell elongate, subelliptical to sublanceolate-subreniform in side view, highest antero-medially; dorsal margin gently convex, somewhat sinuous; ventral margin concave medially; anterior margin rounded, extended below; posterior margin more narrowly curved, extended medially. Left valve larger than right, overreaching right dorsally and postero-ventrally. Valves not strongly convex, greatest convexity posteromedian. Posteromedian section of dorsal valve margins deeply indented.

Valves with narrow subvertical dorsomedian sulcus slightly anterior to middle; four or five narrow concentric ridges lie in anterior part of shell, and a few subvertical very narrow ridges lie in posterior part of shell; midportion of shell with faint reticulations; small smoothed area ventral to median sulcus in adult specimens represents position of muscle scar; general surface very finely and densely pitted.

Hinge formed by terminal elongate elevated flanges and intervening furrow which fit with terminal grooves and bar in left valve. Inner lamellae fairly broad anteriorly, narrower elsewhere; vestibule present terminally; radial canals few and widely spaced. Muscle scar not clearly seen.

Antennule four-segmented beyond basis; distal margin of protopod finely hairy; third podomere much shorter than preceding segment with anterior distal claw and posterior distal seta; fourth podomere with two median and two distal claws anteriorly; ultimate podomere with three terminal setae, the middle one of which is stout and clawlike.

Antenna consists of three poorly differentiated podomeres beyond basis; penultimate podomere long and composed of two fused segments, midanterior and midposterior edges of this podomere with two long setae, distal posterior edge with a small and a large seta; ultimate podomere short and bears two long, stout terminal claws; exopodite three-jointed and reaches to end of terminal claws.

Mandible with four or five bifid teeth on cutting edge, outer pair longer than others; palp four-segmented; second segment with several distal inner setae; third segment with outer distal setae; ultimate segment setaceous terminally.

Maxilla with three setaceous proximal endites of moderate length; endopod a weakly biramous palp in which ventral or inner ramus is the longer, both of which are distally setaceous.

First thoracic leg three-jointed beyond protopodite, latter with distal outer seta; second segment, also with a single distal outer and terminal segment, bears a short claw. Second and third thoracic legs similar to first but progressively larger and longer, with longer setae and terminal claws. Brush-shaped organ appears to lie between first thoracic legs, and each half bears six long setae.

Length of holotype shell 0.63 mm, height 0.26 mm, convexity 0.25 mm.

RELATIONSHIPS: This species is distinguished by its elliptical sublanceolate outline, narrow anteromedian sulcus, and pattern of surface ridges, reticulations, and pits. *C. sagena* Benson and Kaesler (1963, p. 21) from Sonora is more coarsely reticulate than the present species and less elliptical in outline.

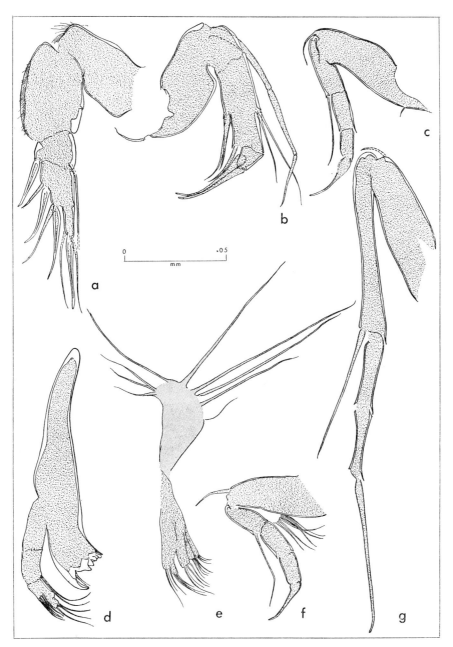

Figure 42. Cushmanidea guardensis *Swain sp. nov., Gulf of California, Station 182.* (a) Antennule; (b) Antenna; (c) Second thoracic leg; (d) Mandible and palp; (e) Maxilla and palp (distorted); (f) First thoracic leg and palp; (g) Third thoracic leg

OCCURRENCE: Recent, Gulf of California, Station 182, depth 6.7 fathoms, sand bottom.
NUMBER OF SPECIMENS STUDIED: 3 (1 living)

Family CYTHERURIDAE Müller, 1894
Genus *Cytherura* Sars, 1866

Cytherura paracostata Swain sp. nov.
(Pl. 9, figs. 17a–d)

Shell elongate-sublanceolate in side view, highest anteromedially; dorsal margin slightly convex, straightened medially; ventral margin nearly straight to slightly concave medially; anterior margin broadly curved, slightly extended below; posterior margin acuminately extended as a ventromedian compressed caudal process. Left valve slightly larger than and extends beyond edge of right. Valves moderately convex, greatest convexity posteromedian.

Dorsal margin with narrow submarginal ridge that continues along terminal margins to midheight; venter also with submarginal ridge that continues along posterior margin to caudal extension, but terminates anteroventrally; two additional prominent longitudinal ridges occur about one-third from dorsal and ventral margins respectively. Several other weak longitudinal ridges are intercalated between main ridges. All ridges flanked by rows of tiny, closely spaced pits. Anteromedian dorsal half of shell surface with narrow, subvertical sulcus.

Hinge of left valve consists of an anterior small socket and posterojacent tooth, interterminal bar formed of narrowed and extended valve edge, and a posterior small socket. Hinge of right valve has corresponding anterior tooth, posterojacent socket, interterminal groove, and posterior tooth. Inner lamellae of moderate width anteriorly, narrower elsewhere; line of concrescence and inner margin widely separated anteriorly; radial canals rather numerous, short and closely spaced. Adductor muscle scar an anteromedian subvertical row of three small, closely spaced spots and one additional antennal spot anterior to dorsal end of main row of spots.

Length of holotype shell 0.32 mm, height 0.17 mm, convexity 0.15 mm.

RELATIONSHIPS: The general shape and longitudinal ridges of this species are similar to features of *C. swaini* van den Bold (1963) from recent deposits of the Gulf of Paria. In that species the posterior caudal extension is longer, and the two longitudinal surface ridges are more median in position.

OCCURRENCE: Recent, Gulf of California, Station 87, depth 7 fathoms, sandy mud bottom; Station 112, depth 34 fathoms, hard clay bottom; Station 175, depth 7.5 fathoms, sand bottom.

NUMBER OF SPECIMENS STUDIED: 6

Cytherura laconica Swain sp. nov.
(Pl. 2, fig. 1)

Shell subovate-reniform in lateral view, highest medially; dorsal margin moderately convex; ventral margin somewhat sinuous, concave anteromedially; anterior margin rounded, somewhat extended below; posterior margin narrower, with blunt dorsomedian compressed caudal process. Left valve slightly larger than right, extending beyond the other dorsally and ventrally but very little or not at all terminally. Valves not markedly convex, greatest convexity posteromedian in position.

Surface ornamented with a pattern of weak, narrow ridges, arranged in a reticulate pattern in posterior half and in a mainly longitudinal pattern anteriorly; anterior margin with a low, narrow submarginal rim; posteroventral narrow marginal zone compressed and extended liplike. A weak eye tubercle occurs anterodorsally. Surface depressed sulcuslike posterior to eye tubercle.

Hinge of right valve consists of terminal, elongate teeth and intervening long grooved edge of valve. Inner lamellae very narrow, line of concrescence and inner margin separated. Muscle scar consists of a short anteromedian vertical row of four closely spaced spots.

Length of holotype shell 0.40 mm, height 0.25 mm, convexity 0.21 mm.

RELATIONSHIPS: As compared to *Cytherura johnsonoides* of the present collection, this species is much less strongly caudate posteriorly.

OCCURRENCE: Recent, Gulf of California, Station 67, depth 4 fathoms, sand bottom; Station 123, depth 5 fathoms, sandy mud bottom.

NUMBER OF SPECIMENS STUDIED: 2

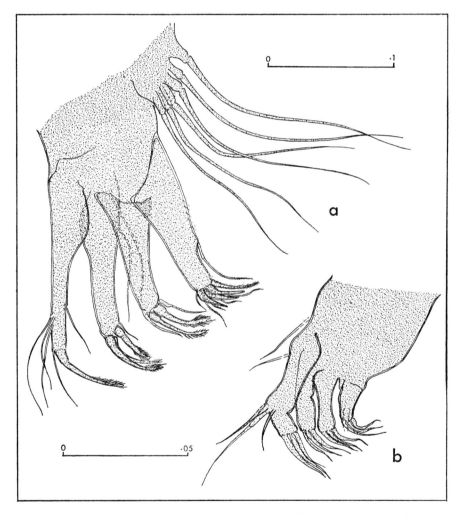

Figure 43. Bairdia *and* Ambostracan. (a) *Bairdia simuvillosa* Swain sp. nov. Scammon Lagoon, Baja California, maxilla; (b) *Ambostracon glauca* (Skogsberg), Gulf of California, Station 67, maxilla

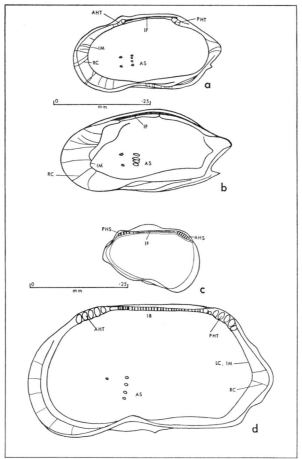

Figure 44. Cytherura *and* Cytheropteron. (a) *Cytherura johnsonoides* Swain sp. nov.,
Gulf of California, Station 102, interior of left valve; (b) *Cytheropteron
dobladoensis* Swain sp. nov., Gulf of California, Station 143, interior of right
valve; (c, d) *Perissocytheridea meyerabichi* (Hartmann), Gulf of California,
Curray's Locality C-80, interiors of immature left valve and mature right
valve

Cytherura johnsonoides Swain sp. nov.
(Fig. 44a; Pl. 2, figs. 2a, b; Pl. 3, figs. 10, 12)

Shell elongate, sublanceolate-subovate in side view, highest slightly posterior to midlength; dorsal margin gently convex; ventral margin less convex than dorsum, somewhat
sinuous anteromedially; anterior margin rounded, extended medially; posterior margin
with dorsomedian blunt caudate extension. Valves of unequal size, left larger than
right. Convexity moderate, greatest in posteroventral part of shell.

Posterior portion of *female?* shell, except compressed end, somewhat swollen; ventral
portion of same shell with low submarginal ridgelike elevation; general surface with
eight to ten narrow longitudinal sinuous ridges, between which occur numerous subvertical but lower crossbars, providing a reticulate pattern of ornamentation. General
surface between ridges faintly pitted. *Male?* shell with similar surface ornamentation
but without posteromedian swelling and ventral longitudinal ridgelike elevation.

Hinge of left valve consists of an anterior small elongate, crenulate socket, an interterminal bar formed of valve edge, and a posterior shorter socket with two or three crenulations; hinge of right valve correspondingly bears terminal crenulate teeth and an interterminal groove; interterminal elements faintly crenulate in well-preserved specimens. Inner lamellae in mature specimens very broad anteriorly, narrower posteriorly; line of concrescence and inner margin coincide; radial canals relatively few (about 15 anteriorly), widely and irregularly spaced, and sinuous. Adductor muscle scar a submedian vertical row of four small, closely spaced spots and a single more-anterior spot near upper end of main group.

Length of holotype left valve 0.40 mm, height 0.22 mm, convexity of valve 0.13 mm.

RELATIONSHIPS: The species is similar to *Cytherura johnsoni* Mincher (1941, p. 343) in general shape and surface ornamentation but is more elongate and has a generally more convex dorsum that *C. johnsoni,* which is straightened dorsomedially.

OCCURRENCE: Recent, Gulf of California, Station 39, depth 21 fathoms, muddy sand bottom; Station 41, depth 45 fathoms, sand bottom; Station 67, depth 4 fathoms, sand bottom; Station 77, depth 3 fathoms, sand bottom; Station 78, depth 10 fathoms, sand bottom; Station 87, depth 7 fathoms, sandy mud bottom; Station 88, depth 8 fathoms, gravel and sand bottom; Station 94, depth 4 fathoms, sand bottom; Station 102, depth 6 fathoms, sand bottom; Station 110, depth 10 fathoms, sand bottom; Station 112, depth 34 fathoms, hard clay bottom; Station 119, depth 31 fathoms, sand bottom; Station 123, depth 5 fathoms, sandy mud bottom; Station 130, depth 62 fathoms, sandy mud bottom; Station 137, depth 7 fathoms, muddy sand bottom; Station 138, depth 17 fathoms, muddy sand bottom; Station 141, depth 10 fathoms, sand bottom; Station 144, depth 6 fathoms, sand bottom; Station 153, depth 18 fathoms, muddy sand bottom; Station 158, depth 17 fathoms, muddy sand bottom; Station 162, depth 13 fathoms, sand bottom; Station 173, depth 220 fathoms, muddy sand bottom; Station 175, depth 7.5 fathoms, sand bottom; Station 179, depth 488 fathoms, mud bottom; Station 182, depth 6.7 fathoms, sand bottom; Station 189, depth 10 fathoms, sand bottom; Station 192, depth 262 fathoms, mud bottom; Station 197, depth 28 fathoms, sandy mud bottom; Station 201, depth 13 fathoms, muddy sand bottom; Station 216, depth 18 fathoms, sandy mud bottom; Station 217, depth 15 fathoms, sandy mud bottom.

NUMBER OF SPECIMENS STUDIED: 25+

Cytherura johnsonoides Swain subspecies a?
(Pl. 3, fig. 9)

A right valve has the following characteristics: outline subovate-subpyriform, highest medially; dorsal margin moderately convex; ventral margin gently convex; anterior margin rounded, extended medially; posterior margin with prominent, but short caudal process, slightly ventral to midheight. Valve moderately convex, greatest convexity ventromedian.

Surface of valve ornamented by about eight longitudinal, curving, sinuous ridges, between which are numerous vertical crossridges, giving a reticulate pattern of ornamentation; shell surface between ridges finely punctate. A low longitudinal ridge occurs midventrally.

Hinge of right valve consists of terminal elongate, weakly crenulate teeth separated by an interterminal deeply incised, also weakly crenulate groove. Inner lamellae broad anteriorly, somewhat narrower ventrally and posteriorly; radial canals number 10 to 12 anteriorly and in part occur in pairs. Muscle scar not observed.

Length of holotype right valve 0.36 mm, height 0.21 mm, convexity of valve 0.11 mm.

RELATIONSHIPS: The general shape and particularly the surface ornamentation of this form are very much like *C. johnsonoides* sensu strictu. The more ventral position of the caudal process and the deep incision of the median part of the hinge of this form are possible reasons for separating it from *johnsonoides.*

OCCURRENCE: Recent, Gulf of California, Station 67, depth 4 fathoms, sand bottom;

Station 102, depth 6 fathoms, sand bottom; Station 126, depth 20 fathoms, sandy mud bottom; Station 179, depth 488 fathoms, mud bottom.

NUMBER OF SPECIMENS STUDIED: 4

Cytherura bajacala Benson
(Pl. 9, fig. 7)

Cytherura bajacala BENSON, 1959, Kansas Univ., Paleont. Contr., Arthropoda, Art. 1, p. 52, Pl. 4, figs. 7a–c, Pl. 9, figs. 1(?), 11, 14

Shell subpyriform-subquadrate in side view, highest medially; dorsal margin moderately convex; ventral margin nearly straight; anterior margin broadly curved; posterior margin with acuminate caudate extension strongly extended below.

Valves subequal, left slightly the larger; valve surfaces strongly inflated in alate midventral region. Ventral surface flattened and slightly overhangs margin in posterior half; narrow knife-edge ridge lies at crest of ventral ala. General surface of valves strongly reticulate, longitudinal ridgelike elements of reticulate pattern more strongly developed in ventral than in dorsal part of shell; anterior and posterior marginal borders of shell compressed and smoooth.

Separate valves not seen; anterior radial canals number about 11 and are irregularly spaced; posterior radial canals few; one long canal on each valve extends into caudal process.

Length of figured specimen 0.40 mm, height 0.22 mm, convexity 0.20 mm.

REMARKS: The outline and surface ornamentation of the species are like *C. bajacala* Benson, although as neither Benson nor the writer have seen all the internal shell structures, identification is somewhat uncertain.

OCCURRENCE: Recent, Gulf of California, Station 142, depth 15 fathoms, sand bottom. The species was originally described from Todos Santos Bay, Baja California, at fairly shallow depths on fine sand bottom (Benson 1959, p. 52).

NUMBER OF SPECIMENS STUDIED: 3

Genus *Cytheropteron* Sars, 1866

Cytheropteron altatensis Swain sp. nov.
(Pl. 9, fig. 10)

Shell sublanceolate in side view, highest medially, except for ala; dorsal margin moderately convex, sloping more or less uniformly away from position of greatest height; ventral margin gently convex except for ala, which projects beyond curvature of margin as viewed laterally; anterior margin rounded, extended medially; posterior margin strongly produced midposteriorly as elongate caudal process. Valve compressed, except for large alate ventral expansion.

Ventral surface with posteriorly directed alate expansion, sharp crest of ala greatly extended posteroventrally as a hollow, flat spine; a short, high, thin flange projects from valve surface posteroventral to ala; a narrow flangelike rim extends along anterior and ventral part of posterior margin; ventral surface of ala with narrow, oblique ridge; general surface smoooth.

Muscle scar a ventromedian vertical row of three elongate, closely spaced spots, and one or two more-anterior spots. Hinge margin of right valve composed of anterior small, beadlike tooth, posterojacent small socket, interterminal arched crenulate furrow, and posterior small tooth. Inner lamellae fairly broad, anteriorly line of concrescence and inner margin are well separated; radial canals few and widely spaced, with scalloped line of concrescence caused by funnel-shaped openings of pore canals.

Length of holotype right valve 0.52 mm, height 0.27 mm, convexity of valve, including ala, 0.27 mm.

RELATIONSHIPS: This species is similar to *C. coryelli* Puri (1954, p. 242) from the Miocene of Florida in general shape, alation, and small subsidiary posteroventral flange, but is more strongly arched dorsally than the Miocene species.

OCCURRENCE: Recent, Gulf of California, Station 52, depth 25 fathoms, sandy mud bottom; Station 21, depth 32 fathoms, mud bottom; Station 39, depth 21 fathoms, muddy sand bottom; Station 41, depth 45 fathoms, sand bottom; Station 112, depth 34 fathoms, hard clay bottom; Station 179, depth 488 fathoms, mud bottom. Named from Altata, Sinaloa Mexico, which lies near sampling Station 52.

NUMBER OF SPECIMENS STUDIED: 6

Cytheropteron caboensis Swain sp. nov.
(Pl. 9, fig. 9)

Shell subpyriform in side view, highest posteromedially; dorsal margin gently convex; ventral margin sinuous, strongly and angularly convex in posterior half due to alation of shell surface; anterior margin narrowly rounded, extended below, with long dorsal slope forming a broadly obtuse cardinal angle with dorsum; posterior margin acuminately curved, extended above, truncate both above and below position of greatest extension. Valves strongly convex in alate posteroventral portion.

Ventral and posteroventral valve surface strongly expanded as a posteriorly directed ala that projects markedly beyond ventral margin and terminates posteriorly in a point; crest of ala sharply angulated and with low ridge; a short narrow ridge lies just dorsal to crest in posterior part of ala; two short, looping ridges lie on broad subvertical, short elevations on dorsal slope of ala; between elevations lie short depressions; marginal zones of valve smooth; anterior portion of general valve surface weakly pitted; posterior portion with several subvertical rows of small pits and intervening furrows; ventral surface of ala with three or four longitudinal ridges of varying length, the median one longer than others.

Hinge margin of left valve bears an anterior socket, an interterminal crenulate bar expanded at posterior end to form a small tooth and with a smaller expansion at anterior end, and a posterior socket. Inner lamellae rather broad anteriorly, narrower posteriorly; radial canals number about 12 anteriorly, and line of concrescence there is slightly scalloped. Adductor muscle scar lies anterior to and ventral to midlength and consists of three or four separated spots in a vertical row and a more-anterior antennal spot.

Length of holotype left valve 0.50 mm, height 0.30 mm, convexity of valve 0.18 mm.

RELATIONSHIPS: In general shape, hingement, and surface ornament, the present species is similar to *Cytheropteron subreticulatum* van den Bold (1946, p. 113) of the Miocene of Cuba and *C. talquinensis* Puri (1953, p. 243) of the Miocene of Florida, but is more strongly alate and has different surface pitting than either species.

OCCURRENCE: Recent, Gulf of California. Named from village of San Jose del Cabo, near collection Station 41, depth 45 fathoms, sand bottom; also from Station 5, depth 1,572 fathoms, mud bottom; Station 86, depth 30 fathoms, sandy mud bottom; Station 192, depth 262 fathoms, mud bottom; Station 204, depth 40 fathoms, muddy sand bottom.

NUMBER OF SPECIMENS STUDIED: 5

Cytheropteron ventrokurtosa Swain sp. nov.
(Fig. 45; Pl. 4, figs. 9a, b; Pl. 9, figs. 11a–d)

Shell subovate in side view, highest anteromedially; dorsal margin moderately convex; ventral margin nearly straight to slightly sinuous, anterior margin broadly rounded, extended below; posterior margin more narrowly curved, extended medially. Valves strongly convex, greatest convexity ventromedian.

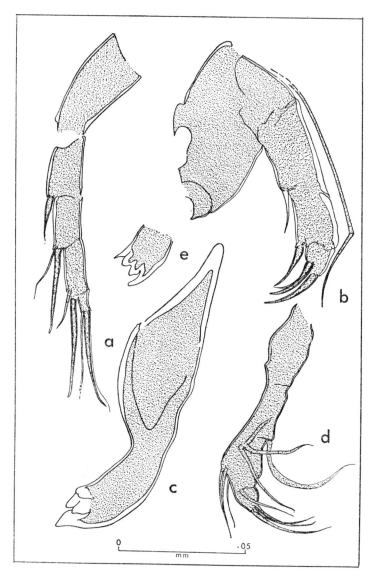

Figure 45. Cytheropteron ventrokurtosa *Swain sp. nov., Scammon Lagoon, Baja California*. (a) Antennule; (b) Antenna; (c) Mandible (coxa); (d) Palp of mandible; (e) Cutting edge of mandible

Ventral surface of valves expanded as a rounded ala that overhangs ventral margin and is somewhat steeper at posterior than at anterior end; crestal part of ala bears three to five longitudinal sinuous narrow ridges; general surface dorsal to ala weakly reticulate.

Hinge of right valve consists of small terminal toothlike ridges and an interterminal crenulate furrow sharply overhung by dorsal margin of valve. Muscle scar consists of a vertical row of four elongate spots and an antennal spot anterior to dorsal end of main group. Inner lamellae of moderate width; line of concrescence and inner margin separated anteriorly and posteroventrally; radial canals relatively few and widely spaced;

line of concrescence somewhat scalloped terminally owing to funnel-shaped opening of pore canals.

Antennule five-segmented; first and second penultimate segments each with a pair of anterior distal setae; ultimate segment bears two long terminal setae.

Antenna composed of three or four poorly differentiated segments; the first beyond the basis is long and composed of about two fused segments; ultimate segment short, with two distal strong claws; exopodite three-jointed, reaching to end of distal claws.

Mandible with four pairs of cutting teeth and an additional inner distal seta; palp three-segmented, with strong distal and inner clawlike setae on penultimate and ultimate segments.

Maxilla has three long clawlike setaceous lobes forming protopod.

Thoracic legs have five podomeres beyond basis, terminal claws slightly curved.

Length of holotype left valve 0.37 mm, height 0.23 mm, convexity of valve 0.13 mm.

RELATIONSHIPS: In general outline, hingement, and short rounded alae, the present species is similar to *C. leonensis* Puri (1954, p. 242) and to *Eocytheropteron yorktownensis* Malkin (1953, p. 780) from the Miocene of Florida and Virginia. The new species, however, has a reticulate valve surface not recorded in *C. leonensis* and is somewhat less umbonate dorsally. It is more coarsely ornamented than *E. yorktownensis*. *Cythere?* sp. cf. *C.? yorktownensis* (Malkin) (Benson and Kaesler, 1963) from the Gulf of California may be the same as the present species, but the illustrations show a different pattern of surface ridges.

OCCURRENCE: Recent, Gulf of California, Station 41, depth 45 fathoms, sand bottom; Station 67, depth 4 fathoms, sand bottom; Station 87, depth 7 fathoms, sandy mud bottom; Station 88, depth 16 fathoms, gravel and sand bottom; Station 102, depth 6 fathoms, sand bottom; Station 110, depth 10 fathoms, sand bottom; Station 112, depth 34 fathoms, hard clay bottom; Station 119, depth 31 fathoms, sand bottom; Station 137, depth 7 fathoms, muddy sand bottom; Station 138, depth 17 fathoms, muddy sand bottom; Station 140, depth 15 fathoms, shell and sand bottom; Station 141, depth 10 fathoms, sand bottom; Station 143, depth 10 fathoms, sand bottom; Station 147, depth 6 fathoms, sand bottom; Station 153, depth 18 fathoms, muddy sand bottom; Station 158, depth 17 fathoms, muddy sand bottom; Station 162, depth 13 fathoms, sand bottom; Station 173, depth 220 fathoms, muddy sand bottom; Station 175, depth 7.5 fathoms, sand bottom; Station 179, depth 488 fathoms, mud bottom; Station 187, depth 13 fathoms, muddy sand bottom; Station 189, depth 10 fathoms, sand bottom; Station 192, depth 262 fathoms, mud bottom; Station 201, depth 13 fathoms, muddy sand bottom; Station 211, depth 10 fathoms, muddy sand bottom; Station 213, depth 8 fathoms, sand bottom; Station 216, depth 18 fathoms, sandy mud bottom; Station 217, depth 15 fathoms, sandy mud bottom.

NUMBER OF SPECIMENS STUDIED: 25 + (2 living)

Cytheropteron assimiloides Swain sp. nov.
(Pl. 9, figs. 8a–c)

Shell subpyriform in side view, highest posteromedially; dorsal margin strongly convex; ventral margin sinuous, strongly convex posteromedially due to extended ala; anterior margin narrowly curved, strongly extended below, and with truncated slope above, grading into dorsal margin; posterior margin with blunt, small caudal process medially; valves compressed except in alate midventral area where they are strongly expanded.

Marginal zone of shell smooth; midventer of each valve with strongly extended, posteriorly pointing ala that markedly overhangs ventral margin; posterodorsally is a low, irregular ridge adjacent to smooth marginal zone; anterior surface of valve with small pits, median surface with larger pits, and posterior surface with small, vertically aligned rows of pits; ala with one or two angular pits on dorsal slope; ventral slope of ala with one or two longitudinal narrow ridges.

Hinge margin of right valve consists of anterior dorsoventrally elongate tooth, interterminal broad vertically crenulate furrow, and posterior vertical tooth; inner lamellae fairly broad, especially at anterior end; line of concrescence and inner margin separate anteriorly and posteroventrally; radial canals numerous and closely spaced.

Length of holotype right valve 0.47 mm, height 0.33 mm, convexity of valve 0.17 mm.

RELATIONSHIPS: The species described here is similar to *C. talquinensis* Puri (1954, p. 243) of the Miocene, and *Cytheropteron assimile* Brady (1880, p. 138) and *C. abyssorum* Brady (1880, p. 138) of the Recent in general outline, alation, and punctate surface; but it has a much more convex dorsal margin and more strongly extended alae than those species.

OCCURRENCE: Recent, Gulf of California, Station 112, depth 34 fathoms, hard clay bottom; Station 130, depth 62 fathoms, sandy mud bottom; Station 144, depth 75 fathoms, muddy sand bottom; Station 179, depth 488 fathoms, mud bottom; Station 204, depth 40 fathoms, muddy sand bottom.

NUMBER OF SPECIMENS STUDIED: 5

Cytheropteron dobladoensis Swain sp. nov.
(Pl. 2, fig. 22; Pl. 3, figs. 11a–c)

Shell alaform-subquadrate in lateral view, highest posteromedially; dorsal margin nearly straight, with broadly obtuse cardinal marginal curvature; ventral margin slightly convex, converging with dorsum in anterior direction; anterior margin rounded, extended medially; posterior margin with sharp dorsomedially projecting caudal compressed process, as well as with projection of ala at ventral marginal bend. Valves moderately convex, venter strongly expanded as a large ala that projects strongly beyond ventral margin and bears a sharp ridge along its crest. Left valve larger than right. General surface of valves rather coarsely reticulate; the longitudinal elements form more or less continuous, sinuous, narrow ridges; width of ridges about half that of intervening pits.

Hinge of right valve rather short and consists of anterior small, rounded tooth; interterminal broad groove; and posterior elongate ridgelike tooth. Inner lamellae broad anteriorly, narrower elsewhere; line of concrescence sinuous; radial canals few, long anteriorly. Muscle scar an anteromedian compact vertical row of four small, closely spaced spots and perhaps one additional anterior spot.

Length of holotype right valve (Pl. 3, fig. 11a) 0.43 mm, height 0.23 mm, convexity of valve 0.15 mm.

RELATIONSHIPS: *Cytheropteron talquinensis* Puri (1954, p. 243) from the Miocene of Florida is similar to the present species in general outline but has alae less posterior in position.

OCCURRENCE: Recent, Gulf of California, Station 39, depth 21 fathoms, muddy sand bottom; Station 143, depth 10 fathoms, sand bottom; Station 144, depth 75 fathoms, muddy sand bottom; Station 119, depth 31 fathoms, sand bottom.

NUMBER OF SPECIMENS STUDIED: 5

Genus *Kangarina* Coryell and Fields, 1937

Kangarina cf. *quellita* Coryell and Fields
(Fig. 46; Pl. 3, figs. 8a, b)

Kangarina quellita CORYELL AND FIELDS, 1937, Am. Mus. Nov., no. 956, p. 13, Figs. 15a–c; PURI, 1954, Florida Geol. Survey Bull. 36, p. 248, Pl. 4, fig. 9; VAN DEN BOLD, 1958, Micropaleontology, v. 4, p. 416, Pl. 4, fig. 8 (See VAN DEN BOLD, 1963, p. 396, for other synonymy.)

Shell subquadrate in lateral view, highest medially; dorsal margin nearly straight, about three-fourths of shell length; anterior cardinal angle broadly obtuse; posterior cardinal marginal bend even more broadly obtuse, less distinct than anterior; ventral

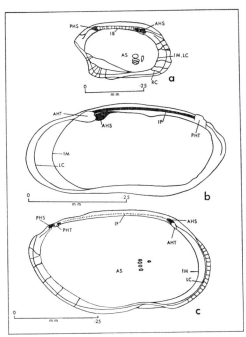

Figure 46. Kangarina, Basslerites, *and* Loxoconcha. (a) *Kangarina quellita* Coryell and Fields, Gulf of California, Station 143, interior of left valve; (b) *Basslerites thlipsuroidea* Swain sp. nov., Gulf of California, Station 194, interior of right valve; (c) *Loxoconcha tamarindoidea* Swain sp. nov., Gulf of California, Station 123, interior of left valve

margin nearly straight to slightly convex, bending abruptly into posterior margin, curving more gradually into anterior margin; anterior margin broadly convex, somewhat extended and weakly spinose below, subtruncate above; posterior margin with blunt, strongly extended caudal process above, concave to markedly truncate below. Valves subequal, the left slightly the larger; moderately convex, greatest convexity ventromedian; posterior end compressed.

Dorsal and anterior margins with low, narrow slightly submarginal rim; a narrow ridge crosses valve obliquely from submedian anterior margin to midventer; two ridges, the anterior the longer, extend subvertically from anterocardinal areas; each joins an oblique dorsomedian longitudinal slightly angulated ridge; a spur extends to margin from posterior end of median ridge, and a short vertical ridge connects anterior end of median ridge with nearby anteroventral ridge; ventral surface of valve flattened; a narrow crestlike ridge occurs at edge of ventral declivity as seen in side view.

Hinge of left valve consists of an anterior small, rounded socket open to rear and posterojacent small tooth, an interterminal crenulate bar formed of valve edge, and a posterior small socket also open to rear. Inner lamellae of moderate width; line of concrescence and inner margin coincide; radial canals few and widely spaced. Muscle scar a slightly anteromedian compact, subvertical row of three or four elongate spots.

Length of figured left valve 0.40 mm, height 0.23 mm, convexity of valve 0.13 mm.

REMARKS: The outline, hingement, and general features of surface ornamentation of this species are like *K. quellita* from the Middle Miocene Gatun Formation of Panama (Coryell and Fields, 1937, p. 13). The details of surface ornamentation in the anterior part of the shell are slightly different from *K. quellita,* and the identification of the Gulf of California specimens is somewhat uncertain.

OCCURRENCE: Recent, Gulf of California, Station 39, depth 21 fathoms, muddy sand bottom; Station 41, depth 45 fathoms, sand bottom; Station 88, depth 8 fathoms, gravel and sand bottom; Station 94, depth 4 fathoms, sand bottom; Station 112, depth 34 fathoms, hard clay bottom; Station 119, depth 31 fathoms, sand bottom; Station 137, depth 7 fathoms, muddy sand bottom; Station 138, depth 12 fathoms, muddy sand bottom; Station 143, depth 10 fathoms, sand bottom; Station 144, depth 75 fathoms, muddy sand bottom; Station 147, depth 6 fathoms, sand bottom; Station 153, depth 18 fathoms, muddy sand bottom; Station 158, depth 17 fathoms, muddy sand bottom; Station 173, depth 220 fathoms, muddy sand bottom; Station 175, depth 7.5 fathoms, sand bottom; Station 179, depth 488 fathoms, mud bottom; Station 187, depth 13 fathoms, muddy sand bottom; Station 189, depth 10 fathoms, sand bottom; Station 192, depth 262 fathoms, mud bottom; Station 197, depth 28 fathoms, sandy mud bottom; Station 204, depth 40 fathoms, muddy sand bottom.

NUMBER OF SPECIMENS STUDIED: 25 +

Genus *Paracytheridea* Müller, 1894

Paracytheridea? pichelinguensis Swain sp. nov.
(Pl. 4, fig. 12; Pl. 8, fig. 2)

Shell elongate, subquadrate in side view, highest near anterior end; dorsal margin nearly straight, about four-fifths of shell length, with very broadly obtuse anterior, but scarcely obtuse posterior cardinal angles; ventral margin nearly straight, slightly sinuous posteriorly; anterior margin broadly curved, slightly extended above, finely spinose; posterior margin narrower, sharply concave above, slightly convex and spinose below, extended medially; valve moderately convex, greatest convexity posteroventral; posterior sixth of valve compressed; anterior fifth also compressed, but less strongly than posterior.

Ventral surface in front of compressed area expanded as an irregularly ridgelike ala, highest near posterior end; a large, rounded, nodelike swelling occurs anterior to mid-length; general surface coarsely pitted or reticulate; anterior margin with smooth elevated border; posterior margin with narrow ridgelike rim.

Hinge margin of right valve with anterior elongate, weakly crenulate, ridgelike tooth; interterminal crenulate furrow; and posterior weakly crenulate tooth; median dorsal interior of valve with subvertical gentle ridge that represents median sulcus in animal. Inner lamella moderately broad; line of concrescence and inner margin slightly separated terminally; radial canals number about 16 anteriorly. Muscle scar a curved row of about four spots lying on posterior flank of median pit.

Length of holotype right valve 0.42 mm, height 0.20 mm, convexity of valve 0.12 mm.

RELATIONSHIPS: The present species somewhat resembles *Paracytheridea nodosa* (Ulrich and Bassler, 1904, p. 129) of the Miocene of eastern United States in general shape, alation, reticulate surface, and median swelling. In that species, however, the ala is more expanded and the posterior margin is not concave as in the present form. Furthermore, the small size of the present specimens makes their generic states somewhat doubtful.

OCCURRENCE: Recent, Gulf of California, Station 67, depth 4 fathoms, sand bottom.

NUMBER OF SPECIMENS STUDIED: 3

Paracytheridea granti LeRoy
(Fig. 47a; Pl. 4, figs. 10, 11a, b; Pl. 5, figs. 1, 2a, b, 3, 4a–c, 5)

Paracytheridea granti LeROY, 1943, Jour. Paleontology, v. 17, p. 361, Fig. 2d; Pl. 61, figs. 11–14, Pl. 62, figs. 3, 4, BENSON, 1959, Kansas Univ. Paleont. Contr. Arthropoda, art. 1, p. 49, Pl. 10, fig. 9

Shell elongate, subpyriform-subquadrate in side view, highest about one-fourth from anterior end; dorsal margin more or less straight, but somewhat sinuous due to projec-

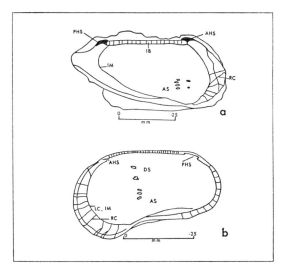

Figure 47. Paracytheridea *and* Limnocythere. (a) *Paracytheridea granti* LeRoy, Gulf of California, Station 143, interior of left valve; (b) *Limnocythere sanctipatricii* Brady and Robertson, Gulf of California, Curray's Locality C-80, interior of right valve

tions of surface ridges beyond margin, about three-fourths of length in left valve but relatively shorter and more sinuous in right valve; posterior cardinal angle greater than anterior, but both are strongly obtuse; ventral margin gently convex but markedly affected by pronounced overhang of alaform expansion in posterior half; anterior margin broadly curved and slightly extended below in left valve, more narrowly curved and extended medially in right valve; posterior margin acuminate, strongly extended above. Left valve a little larger than right, overlapping in cardinal areas; valves strongly inflated mid-ventrally.

Dorsal two-thirds of midvalve surface with a subvertical, narrow, somewhat sinuous sulcus; anterior to sulcus and slightly ventrad of midheight is a median nodelike elevation that is crossed by a longitudinal narrow ridge that continues forward nearly to anterior margin, and a second angular or looplike ridge around margin of elevation; ventral surface strongly alaform, the posterior termination of which lies about one-fourth from posterior end and strongly overhangs ventral margin as a sharp-crested projection; posterocardinal shell surface swollen and, together with rest of surface, bears several sinuous small ridges; characteristically a small marginal spine occurs just ventrad of posterior compressed caudal process; anterior marginal zone of shell compressed.

Hinge of left valve consists of terminal somewhat elongate and crenulate sockets, the posterior comparatively shorter, and an interterminal crenulate bar; hinge of right valve correspondingly consists of terminal elongate crenulate toothlike elevations and an intervening crenulate rabbet groove; inner lamellae of moderate width; no vestibule, radial canals few.

Length of figured left valve (Pl. 5, fig. 2b) 0.63 mm, height 0.31 mm, convexity of valve 0.23 mm.

REMARKS: The details of surface ornamentation and pronounced caudal extension of the shell are distinguishing features of the species.

OCCURRENCE: Recent, Gulf of California, Station 41, depth 45 fathoms, sand bottom; Station 67, depth 4 fathoms, sand bottom; Station 88, depth 16 fathoms, gravel and sand bottom; Station 100, depth 38 fathoms, gravel and sand bottom; Station 112, depth 34 fathoms, hard clay bottom; Station 119, depth 31 fathoms, sand bottom; Station 123, depth 5 fathoms, sandy mud bottom; Station 126, depth 20 fathoms, sandy mud bottom; Station 137, depth 7 fathoms, muddy sand bottom; Station 140, depth 15 fathoms, shell and sand bottom; Station 141, depth 10 fathoms, sand bottom; Station 143, depth 10 fathoms, sand bottom; Station 158, depth 17 fathoms, muddy sand bottom; Station 162, depth 13 fathoms, sand bottom; Station 175, depth 7.5 fathoms, sand bottom; Station 179, depth 488 fathoms, mud bottom; Station 182, depth 6.7 fathoms, sand bottom; Station 197, depth 28 fathoms, sandy mud bottom.

NUMBER OF SPECIMENS STUDIED: 25 +

"Paracytheridea" simplex Swain sp. nov.
(Pl. 2, fig. 16)

Shell elongate-subtrapezoidal in side view, highest posteromedially; dorsal margin half of shell length slightly convex, with broadly convex cardinal angles, the anterior larger than the posterior; ventral margin slightly convex; anterior margin narrowly rounded, strongly extended below; posterior margin bluntly acuminate, strongly extended ventromedially. Valves subequal, moderately convex; greatest convexity median. Surface of valves smooth. Ventral surface of valves flattened, more or less overhanging ventral margin.

Hinge of right valve consists of terminal elongate, faintly denticulate ridges and an interterminal long, recessed section of dorsal margin which bears a weak furrow. Inner lamellae relatively broad anteriorly, where wide vestibule occurs; narrower and without vestibule elsewhere. Radial canals few and widely spaced. Normal canals large and widely spaced. Posterior half of ventral margin extended flangelike. Adductor muscle scar a slightly anteromedian vertical row of four spots and an additional more-anterior antennal spot.

Length of holotype right valve 0.27 mm, height 0.12 mm, convexity of valve 0.08 mm.

RELATIONSHIPS: A species referred to *Cythere wetherellii* Jones from the Middle Miocene of North Carolina (Swain 1952, p. 51) is believed to belong in this genus. It is larger than the present species and has reticulate surface ornamentation. *Paracytheridea similis* Malkin (1953, p. 781) from the Miocene of Virginia is shorter and higher than the present species but otherwise resembles it.

OCCURRENCE: Recent, Gulf of California, Station 88, depth 8 fathoms, gravel and sand bottom; Station 94, depth 4 fathoms, sand bottom; Station 119, depth 31 fathoms, sand bottom; Station 141, depth 10 fathoms, sand bottom; Station 147, depth 6 fathoms, sand bottom; Station 158, depth 17 fathoms, muddy sand bottom; Station 162, depth 13 fathoms, sand bottom; Station 173, depth 220 fathoms, muddy sand bottom; Station 175, depth 7.5 fathoms, sand bottom; Station 179, depth 488 fathoms, mud bottom; Station 187, depth 13 fathoms, muddy sand bottom; Station 197, depth 28 fathoms, sandy mud bottom.

NUMBER OF SPECIMENS STUDIED: 15

Family HEMICYTHERIDAE Puri, 1953
Genus *Hemicythere* Sars, 1925

Hemicythere californiensis LeRoy
(Fig. 48a; Pl. 6, figs. 5a–e)

Hemicythere? californiensis LeRoy, 1943, Jour. Paleontology, v. 17, p. 366, Fig. 2p; Pl. 61, figs. 29–33, Pl. 62, figs. 5, 6; BENSON, 1959, Kansas Univ. Paleont. Contr., Arthropoda, art. 1, p. 65, Pl. 7, fig. 4, Pl. 11, fig. 13
Hemicythere californiensis LeRoy. PURI, 1953, Washington Acad. Sci. Jour., v. 43, p. 174

Shell subpyriform in lateral view, highest anterior to midlength; dorsal margin moderately, but not evenly convex; cardinal angles broadly obtuse, the anterior angle larger

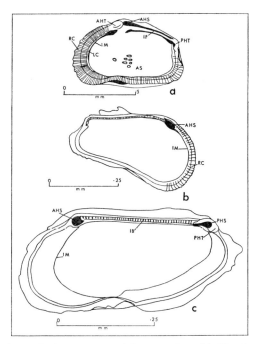

Figure 48. Hemicythere, Ambostracon, *and* Loxoconcha. (a) *Hemicythere californiensis* LeRoy, Gulf of California, Station 153, interior of right valve; (b) *Ambostracon* sp., Gulf of California Station 67, interior of immature left valve; (c) *Loxoconcha?* *emaciata* Swain sp. nov., Gulf of California, Station 189

and less distinct than posterior; ventral margin nearly straight to slightly convex, somewhat sinuous; anterior margin broadly curved, somewhat extended below; posterior margin narrowly rounded, extended below, truncate to slightly concave above. Left valve larger than right, overlapping dorsally and ventrally. Valves moderately convex, greatest convexity somewhat posterior to middle. Posterior fourth of valves compressed.

Surface of shell deeply pitted in a pattern that is concentrically reticulate in marginal two-thirds and has pits more nearly linearly arranged in median third of valves; anterior margin with a narrow pitted compressed rim, defined on inner side by a low narrow ridge that continues along venter to posterior end; medium-sized eye tubercle present anterodorsally.

Hinge of right valve consists of anterior kidney-shaped tooth of which posterior lobe is the higher, posterojacent small triangular socket which passes into long faintly crenulate interterminal furrow, and posterior reniform-oval, smooth tooth; hinge of left valve consists of anterior socket, interterminal bar with anterior expansion, and posterior oval socket. Inner lamellae of moderate width; line of concrescence and inner margin slightly separated terminally; radial canals very numerous and closely spaced terminally, fewer ventrally; right valve with broad selvage furrow, low anteromidventral selvage apophysis, ventral selvage groove, and posterior enclosed selvage groove in extended marginal zone. Muscle scar a slightly anteromedian curved row of four separated spots, a fifth spot just anterior to second spot from top, and two additional, more-anterior antennal spots.

Length of illustrated right valve (Pl. 6, fig. 5c) 0.77 mm, height 0.45 mm, convexity 0.23 mm.

REMARKS: The subovate outline, coarsely pitted surface, and lack of prominent ventral submarginal ridge are characteristic of this species.

OCCURRENCE: Recent, Gulf of California, Station 88, depth 8 fathoms, gravel and sand bottom; Station 153, depth 18 fathoms, muddy sand bottom; Station 162, depth 13 fathoms, sand bottom. Previously recorded from several localities along the coast of California and Baja California from 6 to 30 fathoms depth on coarse to fine sand Shell subpyriform in side view, highest about one-third from anterior end; dorsal margin convex, sloping more steeply in front of than behind position of greatest height; bottoms.

NUMBER OF SPECIMENS STUDIED: 6

Hemicythere? sp. a
(Pl. 6, fig. 2)

ventral margin nearly straight, converging strongly toward posterior with dorsum; anterior margin broadly convex, slightly truncate above; posterior margin subacuminate, strongly extended below, truncate above. Valve compressed, most convex in ventromedian area; posterior fourth of valve compressed.

Anterior and part of dorsal margin with narrow rim; prominent large eye tubercle present; posterodorsal cardinal area with nodelike elevation that projects beyond dorsal margin; an opposed similar but smaller nodelike elevation occurs near ventral margin, and together the two nodes lie at front edge of compressed posterior portion of shell. Venter with submarginal narrow ridge that extends anteriorly from posteroventral node. Anterior to midshell is a low nodelike elevation; general surface deeply and rather coarsely pitted; three diverging longitudinal ridges, part of the pit network, lie anterior to median node.

Hinge of immature right valve consists of an anterior slightly elongate tooth, interterminal crenulate groove, and posterior elongate tooth. Muscle scar lies near midlength, consists of two subvertical parallel rows of four spots and perhaps one additional, more-anterior spot. Inner lamellae scarcely developed in immature specimen at hand.

Length of figured specimen 0.43, height 0.26 mm, convexity of valve 0.10 mm.

REMARKS: The outline, surface ornamentation, and hingement of this species relate it to hemicytherids; but only an immature form is available. It somewhat resembles immature forms assigned to *Quadracythere regalia* Benson (1959, Pl. 11, fig. 3).

OCCURRENCE: Recent, Gulf of California, Station 143, depth 10 fathoms, sand bottom.

NUMBER OF SPECIMENS STUDIED: 1

Hemicythere sp. b
(Pl. 6, figs. 7a, b)

Shell small, subpyriform, highest medially; dorsum strongly arched; venter sinuous, slightly convex posteromedially, slightly concave anteromedially; anterior margin broadly convex, extended below; posterior margin narrowly curved, strongly extended medially; left valve larger than right; valves strongly convex, greatest convexity ventromedian.

Terminal margins compressed flangelike and with narrow rim elevations; general surface coarsely pitted in reticulate pattern; longitudinal ridge elements of reticulum predominant in ventral half; pits of irregular shape in middorsal area.

Hinge of right valve consists of anterior rounded, low tooth, weak posterojacent socket, interterminal faintly crenulate furrow, and posterior low, elongate, faintly crenulate tooth; hinge of left valve comprises an anterior socket, interterminal faintly notched bar and dorsojacent accommodation groove, and a posterior somewhat elongate socket. Inner lamellae broad anteriorly, line of concrescence and inner margin widely separated anteriorly; radial canals rather short except in subcaudate posteromedian area, numerous and closely spaced. Adductor muscle scar not observed in specimens at hand.

Length of figured specimen (Pl. 6, fig. 7b) 0.38 mm, height 0.23 mm, convexity 0.23 mm.

REMARKS: The shape and surface ornamentation of this form resemble *Gangamocytheridea* van den Bold (1963, p. 381), but the hingement is hemicythereid. The line of concrescence and inner margin are widely separated anteriorly, not coincident as in that genus; and the radial canals are numerous as in the Hemicytheridae. This form may represent immature *Aurila conradi californica* Benson, but its relationships are at present uncertain.

OCCURRENCE: Recent, Gulf of California, Station 111, depth 7 fathoms, hard clay bottom.

NUMBER OF SPECIMENS STUDIED: 2

Genus *Ambostracon* Hazel, 1962

Ambostracon vermillionensis Swain sp. nov.
(Pl. 8, figs. 11a–e, 12?)

Shell subquadrate in side view, highest about one-third from anterior margin; dorsal margin nearly straight to slightly sinuous, with broadly obtuse anterior cardinal marginal bend and less obtuse posterior angle; ventral margin slightly concave; anterior margin broadly curved, somewhat extended below; subtruncate above, finely spinose; posterior margin narrowly rounded, strongly extended ventromedially, markedly truncate to concave above, and with five to six blunt serrations below. Left valve larger than right and extends beyond it along dorsal part. Valves not strongly convex; greatest convexity median to ventromedian. Posterior fourth of valves strongly compressed.

Anterior margin with submarginal ridge, lower in ventral than in dorsal half, and enclosing small, glassy eye tubercle dorsally; ventrally ridge continues along margin as narrow, low rim anteriorly and as a narrower, higher ridge posteriorly. Posterior margin also with narrow, low rim. A loop-shaped ridge rises anteromedially, trends across small median tubercle, continues posteriorly and dorsally, bends sharply and obliquely downward toward anterior along dorsum to midlength where it dies out; a spur ridge connects posterodorsal loop with margin of valve; a ventral longitudinal prominent narrow ridge, highest posteromedially, occupies middle two-thirds of valve. General surface of valves with numerous small pits representing position of normal canals.

Hinge of left valve consists of an anterior deep socket and posterojacent tooth, both set on a platform rising from interior valve surface, an interterminal rabbet groove, open above, and a posterior deep, slightly elongate socket, open ventrally. Hinge of right valve consists of an anterior high tooth, posterojacent socket, interterminal rabbet groove open below, and a posterior kidney-shaped tooth. Muscle scars lie in anteromedian depression that represents median external node; scars consist of a main group of six spots occurring in pairs, in addition to which there are three or four more-anterior spots. Inner lamellae of moderate width; line of concrescence and inner margin slightly separated posteroventrally and anteriorly; radial canals numerous anteriorly, relatively fewer posteriorly.

Length of holotype left valve 0.83 mm, height 0.50 mm, convexity of valve 0.23 mm.

RELATIONSHIPS: The details of surface ornamentation of *A. vermillionensis* are characteristic. It differs from *A. costatum* Hazel, the type species, in lacking the complexly branched median ridges of that species and also in having a more compressed and flange-like posterior end of the shell.

OCCURRENCE: Recent, Gulf of California, Station 67, depth 4 fathoms, sand bottom; Station 140, depth 15 fathoms, shell and sand bottom; Station 162, depth 13 fathoms, sand bottom; Station 217, depth 15 fathoms, sandy mud bottom.

NUMBER OF SPECIMENS STUDIED: 8

Ambostracon glauca (Skogsberg)
(Figs. 43b, 52, 53; Pl. 5, figs. 6a–c, 9, 12a, b; Pl. 6, fig. 8; Pl. 9, figs. 16a, b)

Cythereis glauca SKOGSBERG, 1928, California Acad. Sci. Occasional Papers, v. 15, p. 110, Pl. 3, figs. 2, 6, 7; Pl. 4, fig. 4; LUCAS, 1931, Canadian Biol. and Fish. Contr., n.s., no. 17, Pl. 6; LeROY, 1943, Jour. Paleontology, v. 17, p. 368, Pl. 61, figs. 19–23, Fig. 2v, w, Pl. 62, figs. 11, 12; BENSON, 1959, Kansas Univ. Paleont. Contr., art. 1, p. 63., Pl. 6, figs. 1a–c, Pl. 10, fig. 8

Trachyleberis glauca (Skogsberg). CROUCH, 1949, Jour. Paleontology, v. 23, p. 597

Shell variable, subquadrate, either shortened or elongate; highest one-fourth to one-fifth from anterior end; dorsal margin nearly to slightly convex or sinuous, with obtuse cardinal angles, of which anterior is the larger; ventral margin nearly straight and somewhat longer than dorsum, slightly sinuous in right valve and converges toward dorsum posteriorly; anterior margin broadly convex, slightly extended below, subtruncate just beneath cardinal angle; posterior margin narrowly curved and strongly extended to subcaudate below, concave above. Left valve larger than right and extending beyond it in cardinal areas. Valves compressed, greatest convexity posterodmedian in position.

Anterior margin with narrow submarginal rim that becomes lower and weaker along venter, but again is stronger along posterior margin; a second submarginal narrow ridge parallel to venter; a short, thick ridge extends from anterodorsal eye tubercle subparallel to anterior margin to slightly ventrad of midheight; anteromedian node with a sinuous short ridge anterior to it and which trends toward anteroventral margin; a looplike ridge occurs in posterodorsal portion of shell, is thickest near cardinal angle, and encloses a short, lobelike ridge; subsidiary sinuous ridges radiate from median node, and short spurs or reticulating low ridges lie on flanks of larger ridges and occupy main shell surface; a rather prominent oblique groove extends from middorsum to midheight below anterior cardinal angle.

Hinge of right valve consists of anterior knoblike tooth, posterojacent deep socket that opens into interterminal groove, weakly crenulate medially, and a posterior large tooth that bears a few irregularities on its surface. Inner lamellae of moderate width, broadest anteriorly, becoming narrow above midheight posteriorly; line of concrescence and inner margin separated; radial canals very numerous and closely spaced along free margin, except above midheight, posteriorly. Muscle scar lies in large anteromedian pit and consists of a subvertical row of four spots, posterior to middle two of which are two more spots; anteriorly there are three or more spots. Low selvage ridge along inner margin of broad selvage surface of right valve corresponds to selvage furrow in left valve; anteromidventral margin with selvage furrow and apophysis.

Antennule composed of four podomeres beyond basis; first podomere with several anterior distal bristles and posterior seta; second podomere shorter than first and with strong anterior distal seta; third podomere formed by fusion of two with two anterior median and three distal setae; ultimate podomere much narrower and with a pair of long terminal setae.

Antenna of two podomeres beyond basis; first podomere much shorter than basis and sharply geniculate and with two-jointed stout claw from inner distal margin; second podomere long, formed of at least two fused segments, with two median posterior and one anterior setae and three terminal claws. Exopod two-jointed reaching to ends of terminal claws.

Mandible with nine teeth on cutting surface and about four associated setae; palp with three large inner villous setae, a median lobe bearing three terminal setae, and an outer group of four long setae; along midportion of protopod are a villous large branched inner seta and several small outer setae.

Maxilla with three setaceous lobes on protopod and a similar fourth slightly opposed setaceous lobe in front; respiratory palp with about 12 rays, each of which has an enlarged basal part; several lateral setae on palp.

Thoracic legs three-segmented beyond protopodite; latter has a median dorsal and a proximal ventral knurled seta and one (on second and third) and two (on first) distal setae.

Penis as shown in Figure 53k.

Length of right valve 0.95 mm, height 0.50, convexity of valve 0.28 mm.

REMARKS: Type specimens of *Cythereis glauca* in the U.S. National Museum were studied and found to be the same as the present species.

OCCURRENCE: Recent, Gulf of California, Station 41, depth 45 fathoms, sand bottom; Station 67, depth 4 fathoms, sand bottom; Station 88, depth 8 fathoms, gravel and sand bottom; Station 94, depth 4 fathoms, sand bottom; Station 102, depth 6 fathoms, sand bottom; Station 110, depth 10 fathoms, sand bottom; Station 119, depth 31 fathoms, sand bottom; Station 138, depth 17 fathoms, muddy sand bottom; Station 140, depth 15 fathoms, shell and sand bottom; Station 143, depth 10 fathoms, sand bottom; Station 162, depth 13 fathoms, sand bottom; Station 175, depth 7.5 fathoms, sand bottom; Station 182, depth 6.7 fathoms, sand bottom; Station 187, depth 13 fathoms, muddy sand bottom.

NUMBER OF SPECIMENS STUDIED: 25 + (2 living)

Ambostracon sp.
(Pl. 5, fig. 8)

Immature left valve, elongate subtrapezoidal, highest near anterior end; dorsal margin nearly straight, irregular posteriorly owing to projecting nodes, with obtuse cardinal angles, of which anterior is larger than posterior; ventral margin slightly concave; anterior margin broadly rounded, somewhat extended below, truncate above; posterior margin much narrower than anterior, with strong truncated projection below, concave above. Valve compressed, greatest convexity one-third from posterior end, behind which position shell strongly compressed.

Anterior, ventral, and posterior margins with low, narrow, elevated rim; rounded glassy eye tubercle occurs at anterodorsal cardinal angle; median rounded, elevated node marks position of adductor muscle scar; midventral surface with ridgelike swelling that becomes higher posteriorly and terminates in nodelike elevation one-fourth from posterior end; posterodorsally are two oblique short, strongly elevated ridges that project beyond valve margin; a low ridge extends anteriorly from median node, and there are several other nodes scattered over weakly reticulate surface.

Hinge of left valve consists of anterior socket, posterojacent low juvenile toothlike ridge, interterminal faintly crenulate bar, and posterior elongate socket; adductor muscle scar an oblique row of three or four elongate spots lying in median pit; inner lamellae not developed in present specimen; ventroposterior margin with short flangelike extension; radial canals numerous and closely spaced.

Length of figured left valve 0.48 mm, height 0.27 mm, convexity of valve 0.13 mm.

REMARKS: The general outline, hingement, radial canals, and surface ornamentation ally this form with *Ambostracon* Hazel; but only an immature specimen was observed.

OCCURRENCE: Recent, Gulf of California, Station 67, depth 4 fathoms, sand bottom.

NUMBER OF SPECIMENS STUDIED: 1

Genus *Aurila* Pokorny, 1955

Aurila conradi californica Benson and Kaesler
(Fig. 49a; Pl. 6, fig. 3, 6a–d)

Brachycythere schumannensis (LeRoy). BENSON, 1959, Kansas Univ. Paleont. Contr., Arthropoda, art. 1; p. 49, Pl. 3, figs. 3a, b, Pl. 11, fig. 11

Aurila conradi californica BENSON AND KAESLER, 1963, Kansas Univ. Paleont. Contr., Arthropoda, art. 3; p. 23, Fig. 12; Pl. 1, figs. 9, 10

Shell subovate, shortened, almond-shaped in side view, highest medially; dorsal

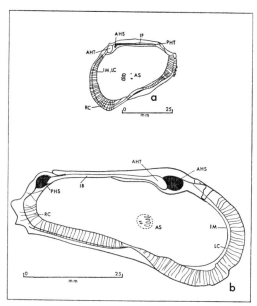

Figure 49. Aurila *and* Caudites. (a) *Aurila conradi californica* Benson and Kaesler, Gulf of California, Station 137, interior of right valve; (b) *Caudites rosaliensis* Swain sp. nov., Gulf of California, Station 189, interior of left valve

margin strongly convex; ventral margin gently convex, slightly sinuous; anterior margin broadly curved, slightly extended below; posterior margin narrowly curved, subacuminate, and extended below, truncate to slightly concave above. Left valve larger than right, extending beyond right along dorsal and anterior margins. Valves strongly convex; greatest convexity slightly posteromedian.

Valves with narrow, smooth, not greatly elevated marginal rim; terminal marginal zones compressed; a longitudinal low ridge parallels venter close to margin; anterodorsal eye tubercle with weak subjacent furrow in right valve; terminal margins of both valves finely denticulate; general surface coarsely pitted in submarginal areas with a reticulate pattern.

Hinge of right valve consists of an anterior high, oblong tooth; posterojacent deep, rounded socket; interterminal weakly crenulate groove; and posterior, elongate, denticulate tooth. Hinge of left valve correspondingly consists of anterior deep socket, adjacent high tooth, and interterminal crenulate bar, dorsal to which is a deep, wide accommodation groove.

Muscle scar consists of a curving median row of four spots and at least one additional, more-anterior spot. Inner lamellae broad anteriorly and posteroventrally; line of concrescence and inner margin nearly coincide; radial canals very numerous and closely spaced anteriorly and posteroventrally. Midventral incurved area of shell with prominent selvage apophysis in right valve and corresponding selvage furrow in left valve.

Length of figured specimen (Pl. 6, fig. 6c) 0.68 mm, height 0.43 mm, convexity 0.40 mm.

REMARKS: The surface ornamentation of this species is less coarse than in *Aurila conradi* Howe and McGuirt (in Howe and others, 1935, p. 27) but the shape and internal features are otherwise close to that species; *Aurila lincolnensis* (LeRoy) (1943, p. 364) and subspecies *schumannensis* from the later Tertiary and Quaternary of California are of similar shape but have more subdued surface ornamentation. *Aurila driveri* (LeRoy) (1943, p. 361) from the late Pliocene of California is more rugosely ornamented than *A. schumannenis*. There is some uncertainty as to the relationship of the present specimens to

A. conradi californica Benson and Kaesler, but to the writer the two appear to be nearly identical.

OCCURRENCE: Recent, Gulf of California, Station 19, depth 8 fathoms, sand bottom; Station 41, depth 45 fathoms, sand bottom; Station 49, depth 390 fathoms, mud bottom; Station 67, depth 4 fathoms, sand bottom; Station 87, depth 7 fathoms, sandy mud bottom; Station 88, depth 8 fathoms, gravel and sand bottom; Station 94, depth 4 fathoms, sand bottom; Station 100, depth 38 fathoms, gravel and sand bottom; Station 102, depth 6 fathoms, sand bottom; Station 110, depth 10 fathoms, sand bottom; Station 111, depth 7 fathoms, hard clay bottom; Station 112, depth 34 fathoms, hard clay bottom; Station 119, depth 31 fathoms, sand bottom; Station 123, depth 5 fathoms, sandy mud bottom; Station 130, depth 62 fathoms, sandy mud bottom; Station 137, depth 7 fathoms, muddy sand bottom; Station 138, depth 17 fathoms, muddy sand bottom; Station 140, depth 15 fathoms, shell and sand bottom; Station 141, depth 10 fathoms, sand bottom; Station 142, depth 15 fathoms, sand bottom; Station 143, depth 10 fathoms, sand bottom; Station 144, depth 75 fathoms, muddy sand bottom; Station 152, depth 220 fathoms, sandy mud bottom; Station 153, depth 18 fathoms, muddy sand bottom; Station 158, depth 17 fathoms, muddy sand bottom; Station 175, depth 45 feet, sand bottom; Station 179, depth 488 fathoms, mud bottom; Station 182, depth 6.5 fathoms, sand bottom; Station 187, depth 13 fathoms, muddy sand bottom; Station 189, depth 10 fathoms, sand bottom; Station 192, depth 262 fathoms, sand bottom; Station 194, depth 75 fathoms, muddy sand bottom; Station 195, depth 75 fathoms, sandy mud bottom; Station 199, depth 28 fathoms, sandy mud bottom; Station 201, depth 13 fathoms, muddy sand bottom; Station 213, depth 8 fathoms, sand bottom; Station 216, depth 10 fathoms, sandy mud bottom; Station 217, depth 15 fathoms, sandy mud bottom. The species has also been recorded from the Pleistocene of Southern California (LeRoy, 1943) and from the Estero de Tastiota, Sonora, Mexico (Benson and Kaesler, 1963).

NUMBER OF SPECIMENS STUDIED: 25 +

Aurila convergens Swain sp. nov.
(Pl. 8, fig. 8)

Shell subovate, almond-shaped in lateral view, highest one-third from anterior end; dorsal margin moderately convex, sloping more steeply anterior to, than posterior to position of greatest height; ventral margin slightly concave medially, otherwise nearly straight; anterior margin broadly curved, slightly extended below; posterior margin much narrower in total curvature, strongly extended below, concave above. Left valve larger than right, overlapping right and extending beyond it dorsally and midventrally; valves moderately convex, greatest convexity median; posterior sixth of valves compressed.

Anterior marginal zone with narrow submarginal ridge that continues across rounded eye tubercle along dorsum to midlength; ventral margin with very narrow knife-edged ridge; a longitudinal ventral ridge, highest about one-fifth from posterior end, extends from anteroventral marginal bend to posterior end; a curving ridge extends from a point near anterior end of submarginal ventral ridge and about one-sixth from anterior end dorsally and posteriorly subparallel to shell margin, attaining greatest height posterodorsally and terminating in a ventral curvature in posterodorsal region; midportion of valve with four longitudinal, anteriorly converging, rather strongly elevated ridges, middle two of which bifurcate in a posterior direction; numerous low crossbars between surface ridge provide a pseudoreticulate pattern to shell; a narrow, hook-shaped ridge, open anterodorsally, lies across median longitudinal ridge. Internal structures mainly not observed; radial canals numerous and closely spaced terminally, fewer ventrally.

Length of holotype shell 0.53 mm, height 0.32 mm, convexity 0.25 mm.

RELATIONSHIPS: The outline and main features of surface ornamentation, as well as the numerous radial canals, relate this species to *Aurila* Pokorny. The pattern of strong, anteriorly converging ridges appear to be unique in this species. *Hemicythere punctis-triata* (Ulrich and Bassler, 1904) from the Miocene of Maryland is similar in shape and ornamentation but is more elongate and has weaker ridges than the present species. *Brachychthere* sp. (Benson, 1959, Pl. 11, fig. 2) is similar in shape but has different surface ornamentation than the new species.

OCCURRENCE: Recent, Gulf of California, Station 137, depth 7 fathoms, muddy sand bottom.

NUMBER OF SPECIMENS STUDIED: 3

Genus *Caudites* Coryell and Fields, 1937

Caudites rosaliensis Swain sp. nov.
(Figs. 50a–c, 51a–e; Pl. 5, figs. 10a, b, 11, 13a–e)

Shell subquadrate to subtrapezoidal in side view, highest about one-third from anterior end; dorsal margin nearly straight with broadly obtuse anterior cardinal angle and much less obtuse posterior cardinal angle; ventral margin slightly concave to nearly straight; anterior margin broadly curved, somewhat extended below, subtruncate above; posterior margin bluntly acuminate, strongly extended below, concave above. Left valve slightly larger than right, extending beyond right in cardinal areas. Valves not strongly convex, greatest convexity median.

Anterior margin of each valve provided with irregularly nodose and spurred rim; dorsal margin with submarginal ridge in anterior half which connects with anterior rim through large eye tubercle; posterior portion of dorsal margin also with ridge that begins submarginally anteriad of midlength and extends posteriorly, close to margin to about one-sixth from posterior end, where it rises to a low, pointed node and bends at right angles ventrally to, or nearly to, venter; surface posterior to this ridge compressed and posterior margin with narrow elevated rim; most of ventral surface with narrow, moderately elevated submarginal longitudinal ridge; ventral margin also with narrow rim; anterior margin very finely and abundantly spinose; between anterior margin and submarginal ridge are six to eight narrow crossridges; a spurlike ridge extends obliquely forward and downward from posterodorsal bend of submarginal ridge; in mature shells this spur reaches to median low, nodelike swelling; flanks of median and of inner parts of posterior submarginal ridges with small spurlike extensions that are lacking in immature shells.

Hinge of right valve consists of an anterior high, pointed tooth, posterojacent socket, interterminal furrow, and posterior bluntly pointed tooth faintly notched on its inner slope. Hinge of left valve correspondingly consists of anterior socket, posterojacent tooth, interterminal bar, and posterior socket. Inner lamellae very broad anteriorly, much narrower ventrally and posteriorly; line of concrescence and inner margin widely separated anteriorly; radial canals very numerous and closely spaced anteriorly. Adductor muscle scar consists of a median vertical row of four spots, anterior to ventral two of which are two additional spots, and well anterior to main group are three antennal spots.

Antennule with six podomeres, proximal two about twice length of others; second podomere with about six setae, one of posterior of which very long; third podomere with distal stout anterior seta; fourth and fifth podomeres nearly fused, but latter much narrower, fourth with stout distal anterior and two smaller seae; fifth podomere also with strong distal anterior seta; sixth podomere much narrower than others, with one anterior seta and one terminal claw.

Antenna with two long geniculate podomeres, of which second apparently represents fusion of three podomeres and an additional short ultimate podomere that bears three distal claws; second podomere with three posterior setae at positions representing distal margins of fused segments; exopodite reaches about to end of distal claws.

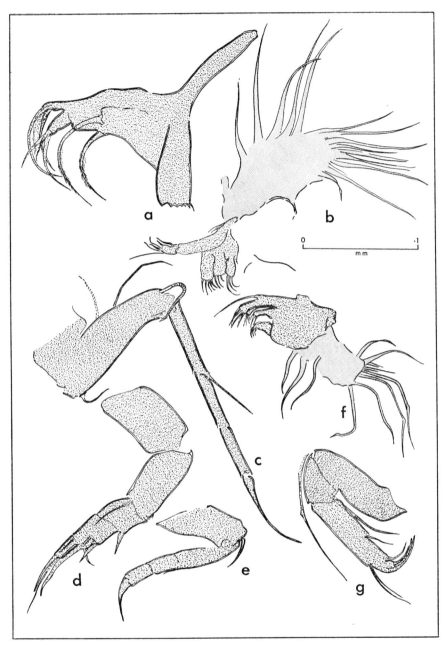

Figure 50. Caudites *and* Orionina. (a–c) *Caudites rosaliensis* Swain sp. nov., Gulf of California, Station 189; (a) Mandible and palp; (b) Maxilla and respiratory lobe; (c) Third? thoracic leg; (d–g) *Orionina pseudovaughani* Swain sp. nov., Gulf of California, Station 78; (d) Antennule; (e) First? thoracic leg; (f) Maxilla and respiratory lobe; (g) Antenna.

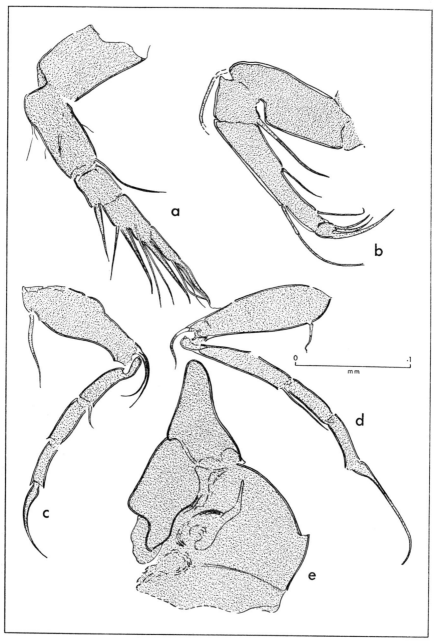

Figure 51. Caudites rosaliensis *Swain sp. nov., Gulf of California, Station 189.* (a) Antennule; (b) Antenna; (c) First thoracic leg; (d) Second thoracic leg; (e) Penis

Mandible with six short serrations and a small posterior seta, palp with four claws on basis and two claws on endopod.

Maxilla with three setaceous proximal endites, exopod of two segments, bearing five distal setae, vibratory palp with about fifteen plumes.

Thoracic legs four-jointed; protopodite with one or two knurled distal setae, second segment with distal anterior seta; terminal claws exceed length of ultimate segment.

Length of holotype (female) shell 0.65 mm, height 0.38 mm, convexity 0.30 mm.

RELATIONSHIPS: The surface ridges, although variably developed, are generally stronger than in other species of the genus. *C. serrata* Benson and Kaesler (1963) from the Recent of Sonora, Mexico, does not have the postmedian longitudinal ridge that characterizes mature specimens of the present species and differs in other features of surface ornamentation.

OCCURRENCE: Recent, Gulf of California, Station 4, depth 45 fathoms, sand bottom; Station 39, depth 212 fathoms, muddy sand bottom; Station 67, depth 4 fathoms, sand bottom; Station 88, depth 16 fathoms, gravel and sand bottom; Station 94, depth 4 fathoms, sand bottom; Station 110, depth 10 fathoms, sand bottom; Station 111, depth 7 fathoms, hard clay bottom; Station 123, depth 973 fathoms, mud bottom; Station 137, depth 7 fathoms, muddy sand bottom; Station 140, depth 15 fathoms, shell and sand bottom; Station 141, depth 0.6 fathoms, sand bottom; Station 143, depth 10 fathoms, sand bottom; Station 147, depth 5.8 fathoms, sand bottom; Station 153, depth 18 fathoms, muddy sand bottom; Station 158, depth 17 fathoms, muddy sand botom; Station 162, depth 13 fathoms, sand bottom; Station 175, depth 7.5 fathoms, sand bottom; Station 187, depth 13 fathoms, muddy sand bottom; Station 189, depth 10 fathoms, sand bottom; Station 213, depth 8 fathoms, sand bottom; Station 217, depth 15 fathoms, sandy mud bottom.

NUMBER OF SPECIMENS STUDIED: 25 + (1 living)

Genus *Mutilus* Neviani, 1928

Mutilus confragosa (Edwards)
(Fig. 52a; Pl. 6, fig. 1a, b)

Hemicythere confragosa EDWARDS, 1944, p. 518, Pl. 86, figs. 23–26; Swain, 1952, U. S. Geol. Survey Prof. Paper 234-A p. 43, Pl. 6, figs. 13, 14; PURI, 1953, Washington Acad. Sci. Jour., v. 43, p. 176, Pl. 1, figs. 4–6; PURI, 1954, Florida Geol. Survey Bull. 36, p. 266, Pl. 11, figs. 10–12; van den Bold, 1958, Micropaleontology, v. 4, p. 71; BROWN, 1958, North Carolina Dept. Conserv. Bull. 72, p. 66, Pl. 7, fig 1

Mutilus confragosa (Edwards). PURI, 1960, Gulf Coast Assoc. Geol. Soc., v. 10, p. 130

Aurila confragosa (Edwards). VAN DEN BOLD, 1963, Micropaleontology, v. 9, p. 325, Pl. 8, fig. 1

Shell subovate-subquadrate in side view, highest medially; dorsal margin moderately convex; ventral margin nearly straight, its outline affected by overhanging subalate ventral ridge in posteroventral region; anterior margin broadly curved, slightly extended below; posterior margin narrowly curved and strongly extended ventromedially, sharply concave above. Valves moderately convex, greatest convexity median; left valve larger than right.

Surface of valves with narrow submarginal ridge along anterior end and anterior two-thirds of dorsal margin; a groove separates ridge from outer margin; a prominent longitudinal narrow ridge, subalate posteriorly, occupies nearly all of ventral submarginal area and has short posterior forklike extension; general surface bears six additional longitudinal ridges occurring more or less in pairs; dorsal pair occupy middle half of valve, are joined at each end, and have three crossbars; median pair extend about two-thirds of valve length, diverge and are joined by a prominent narrow ridge posteriorly, and have about nine crossbars; ventral pair somewhat shorter than median pair and

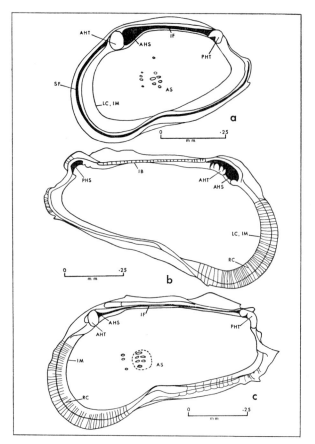

Figure 52. Mutilus *and* Ambostracon. (a) *Mutilus confragosa* (Edwards), Gulf of California, Station 143, interior of right valve; (b, c) *Ambostracon glauca* (Skogsberg), Gulf of California; (b) Station 67, interior of left valve; (c) Station 119, interior of right valve

has about seven crossbars; posterior fifth of valve compressed and has several short ridges; small eye tubercle lies anterodorsally on submarginal ridge.

Hinge of right valve with prominent high, pointed, notched tooth; posterojacent deep, rounded socket; interterminal faintly crenulate groove; and a posterior high, curving tooth. Muscle scar consists of a median subvertical curved row of four rounded spots, two spots anterior to middle two of row, and three additional, more-anterior spots arranged in a subvertical row. Inner lamellae fairly broad, especially anteriorly, line of concrescence and inner margin nearly coincide; radial canals nearly invisible in specimen at hand but apparently numerous and closely spaced. Right valve with well-developed selvage groove and anteromidventral selvage apophysis.

Length of figured right valve, 0.70 mm, height 0.42 mm, convexity of valve 0.20 mm.

REMARKS: The general shape, musculature, and hingement of this form ally it to *Hemicythere* Sars and to *Procythereis* Skogsberg and *Aurila* Pokorny; but the ridge-pattern of surface ornamentation furnishes, in the writer's view, a comparison with *Mutilus* Neviani.

OCCURRENCE: Recent, Gulf of California, Station 41, depth 45 fathoms, sand bottom;

Figure 53. Ambostracon glauca *Skogsberg, Scammon Lagoon, Baja California.* (a) Antennule; (b) Antenna; (c) Palp of mandible; (d) Coxa of mandible; (e) Second thoracic leg; (f) Third thoracic leg; (g) First thoracic leg; (h) Maxilla and respiratory lobe; (i) Vas deferens; (j) Brush-shaped organ; (k) Penis

Station 60, depth 1,480 fathoms; Station 67, depth 4 fathoms, sand bottom; Station 69, depth 395 fathoms, mud bottom; Station 86, depth 30 fathoms, sandy mud bottom; Station 88, depth 8 fathoms, gravel and sand bottom; Station 94, depth 4 fathoms, sand bottom; Station 102, depth 6 fathoms, sand bottom; Station 111, depth 7 fathoms, hard clay bottom; Station 119, depth 31 fathoms, sand bottom; Station 123, depth 5 fathoms, sandy mud bottom; Station 126, depth 20 fathoms, sandy mud bottom; Station 137, depth 7 fathoms, muddy sand bottom; Station 138, depth 17 fathoms, muddy sand bottom; Station 143, depth 10 fathoms, sand bottom; elsewhere it occurs in Upper Miocene and younger deposits of the Atlantic Coastal Plain.

NUMBER OF SPECIMENS STUDIED: 25 +

Genus *Orionina* Puri, 1954

Orionina pseudovaughani Swain sp. nov.
(Figs. 50d–g, 54c; Pl. 3, figs. 5a, b, 13; Pl. 4, figs. 6a–c)

Shell elongate-subquadrate in lateral view, highest medially to anteromedially; dorsal margin gently convex; ventral margin concave medially; anterior margin broadly convex; posterior margin extended and narrowly curved below, truncate to slightly concave above.

Valves compressed, greatest convexity posteromedian; left valve slightly larger than right. Rounded eye tubercle rather prominent anterodorsally; terminal margins with narrow rims; two prominent longitudinal ridges extend from near anterior end to about one-sixth from posterior end, diverging in that direction; at posterior termination a connecting crossridge occurs, and this feature defines posterior compressed end of shell; small submedian node lies between ridges, two-fifths from anterior end; middorsal region bears a somewhat oblique ridge; ventral longitudinal ridge has in anterior half of shell a curving subsidiary ridge closer to margin; general valve surface coarsely reticulated.

Hinge of right valve consists of an anterior rounded tooth; posteriorly adjacent oblong socket; interterminal narrow groove; and posterior, slightly reniform tooth. Inner lamellae broad anteriorly, narrower ventrally and posteriorly; line of concrescence highly irregular owing to development of circular pillars at intervals in zone of concrescence; three additional rounded pillars occur in vestibule between inner margin and line of concrescence; radial canals rather numerous and closely spaced between pillars, anteriorly. Muscle scar consists of a slightly anteromedian vertical row of four spots, and two spots split off anteriorly to middle two of main row; at least one and perhaps additional antennal spots lie anteriad of those just mentioned.

Antennule consists of six podomeres; proximal two segments of equal length and about twice as long as other segments; third and fourth segments each with one short, stout dorsal seta; penultimate segment with two longer dorsal setae; ultimate segment much narrower than others, with two or three terminal setae.

Antenna with five podomeres; second segment much shorter than proximal one; exopodite extends to distal end of endopodites; third and fourth segments fused, with two short ventral, and one long dorsal, setae; penultimate segment with one ventral seta; and ultimate segment with three terminal claws.

Mandibular palp with three setaceous short lobes.

Thoracic legs five-segmented, with stout terminal claws; proximal segment with single anterior seta.

Length of holotype right valve 0.82 mm, height 0.40 mm, convexity of valve 0.17 mm.

RELATIONSHIPS: The outline, hingement, and surface ornamentation of the species are closely similar to *O. vaughani* (Ulrich and Bassler, 1904) from the Miocene. In that species, however, the anterior vestibule has four variably sized pillars rather than three, as in the present species. The form figured by van den Bold (1963) as *O.* aff. *vaughani* from the Miocene of Trinidad may be conspecific with the new species. *O. serrulata* Brady (van den Bold, 1963) may be the same as the present species, but

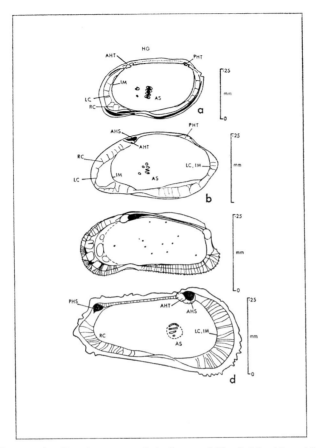

Figure 54. Loxoconcha, Paradoxostoma, Orionina, *and* Trachyleberidea. (a) *Loxoconcha tamarindoides* Swain sp. nov., Gulf of California, Station 213, interior of right valve; (b) *Paradoxostoma multipunctata* Swain sp. nov., Gulf of California, Station 102, interior of right valve; (c) *Orionina pseudovaughani* Swain sp. nov., Gulf of California, Station 78, interior of right valve; (d) *Trachyleberidea tricornis* Swain sp. nov., Gulf of California, Station 143, interior of left valve

serrulata is said to have five rather than three pillars; besides, its taxonomic history is so confused as to make its identity uncertain.

OCCURRENCE: Recent, Gulf of California, Station 27, depth 1,580 fathoms, mud bottom; Station 41, depth 45 fathoms, sand bottom; Station 78, depth 10 fathoms, sand bottom; Station 86, depth 30 fathoms, sandy mud bottom; Station 88, depth 8 fathoms, gravel and sand bottom; Station 94, depth 4 fathoms, sand bottom; Station 102, depth 6 fathoms, sand bottom; Station 110, depth 10 fathoms, sand bottom; Station 119, depth 31 fathoms, sand bottom; Station 123, depth 5 fathoms, sandy mud bottom; Station 137, depth 7 fathoms, muddy sand bottom; Station 141, depth 10 fathoms, sand bottom; Station 153, depth 18 fathoms, muddy sand bottom; Station 158, depth 17 fathoms, muddy sand bottom; Station 162, depth 13 fathoms, sand bottom; Station 173, depth 220 fathoms, muddy sand bottom; Station 187, depth 13 fathoms, muddy sand bottom; Station 201, depth 13 fathoms, muddy sand bottom; Station 213, depth 8 fathoms, sand bottom.

NUMBER OF SPECIMENS STUDIED: 23 (1 living)

Family LEGUMINOCYTHERIDEIDAE Howe, 1961
Genus *Leguminocythereis* Howe, 1936

?Leguminocythereis corrugata LeRoy
(Figs. 33g–m; Pl. 2, figs. 12a, b)

Leguminocythereis corrugata LEROY, 1943, Jour. Paleontology, v. 17, p. 372, Fig. 2x;
Pl. 59, figs. 7–12, Pl. 62, figs. 7, 8; BENSON, 1959, Kansas Univ. Paleont. Contr.,
Arthropoda, art. 1, p. 68, Pl. 4, fig. 1; not *L. corrugata* SWAIN, 1946, Jour. Paleontology,
v. 10, p. 379, Pl. 54, figs. 14a–c, Pl. 55, figs. 5a, b

Shell elongate-subovate in side view, highest about one-third from anterior end;
dorsal margin nearly straight with broadly obtuse, poorly defined anterior cardinal
marginal bend, much less obtuse, better defined posterior cardinal angle; ventral margin
gently convex, converging posteriorly with dorsum; anterior margin broadly rounded,
slightly extended below; posterior margin more narrowly curved, extended medially,
subtruncate above. Valves subequal, the left slightly the larger; convexity of valves
moderate, greatest inflation median in position.

A low swelling occurs anteromedially and is defined posteriorly by a shallow subvertical
furrow; anterior and ventral portions of valves with two or three subparallel narrow,
weak concentric ridges; posterior and median parts of valve with weak longitudinal ridges;
general surface faintly reticulate owing to crossbars between concentric and longitudinal
ridges.

Hinge of left valve consists of an anterior elongate smooth socket groove, interterminal
bar formed of narrow valve edge, and a posterior weak socket. Inner lamellae narrow,
line of concrescence and inner margin separate; radial canals short, numbering about
15 anteriorly. Muscle scar a median subvertical row of three closely spaced, small,
elongate spots and at least one additional, more-anterior antennal spot.

Antennule five-segmented beyond basis, with strongly developed dorsal marginal setae
on distal edges of segments; ultimate podomere with three long swimming setae.
Antenna with three podomeres beyond basis and with stout ventral setae and a terminal
claw. Mandible bears three bifid teeth on cutting edge; palp two-segmented and with
strong ventral setae and two terminal claws. Thoracic legs four-segmented.

Length of left valve (Pl. 2, fig. 12a) 0.84 mm, height 0.43 mm, convexity of valve
0.20 mm.

REMARKS: The shape of the shell of this species is similar to that of *Campylocythere
concinnoidea* Swain (1955, p. 636) from the Recent of San Antonio Bay, Texas. The
presence of surface ridges and median node, rather than surface pits, and particularly
the hingement of the present species distinguish it from *C. concinnoidea*.

OCCURRENCE: Recent, Gulf of California, Station 5, depth 1,572 fathoms, mud bottom;
Station 21, depth 32 fathoms, mud bottom; Station 23, depth 7 fathoms, sand bottom;
Station 39, depth 21 fathoms, muddy sand bottom; Station 78, depth 10 fathoms, sand
bottom; Station 87, depth 7 fathoms, sandy mud bottom; Station 194, depth 75 fathoms,
muddy sand bottom.

NUMBER OF SPECIMENS STUDIED: 10 (1 living)

Genus *Basslerites* Howe, 1937

Basslerites delrayensis LeRoy
(Pl. 8, fig. 14)

Basslerites delrayensis LEROY, 1943, p. 368, Fig. 2k; Pl. 59, figs. 23–27, Pl. 62, figs. 21, 22;
BENSON, 1959, p. 69, Pl. 4, figs. 2a, b, Pl. 8, fig. 5

Shell subelliptical in side view, highest posteromedially; dorsal and ventral margins
gently convex; anterior margin rather narrowly rounded, slightly extended below;

posterior margin broadly curved. Left valve slightly larger than right. Surface smooth. Valves moderately convex posteromedially.

Hinge of left valve consists of anterior socket supported below by a pillarlike process; posterojacent pointed tooth; interterminal nand dorsally adjacent accommodation groove, and a posterior socket. Inner lamellae fairly narrow, line of concrescence and inner margin only slightly separated; radial canals numerous and closely spaced. Muscle scar not seen in present material but is illustrated by LeRoy.

Length of figured left valve, 0.48 mm, height 0.30 mm, convexity of valve 0.15 mm.

OCCURRENCE: Recent, Gulf of California, Station 41, depth 45 fathoms, sand bottom; Station 201, depth 13 fathoms, muddy sand bottom. It was described from the Pleistocene of Southern California and has also been reported from Todos Santos Bay, Ensenada, Mexico.

NUMBER OF SPECIMENS STUDIED: 2

Basslerites thlipsuroidea Swain sp. nov.
(Fig. 46b; Pl. 2, figs. 10a, b)

Shell subelliptical in side view, highest medially; dorsal margin slightly convex; ventral margin very slightly convex, sinuous medially; anterior margin broadly curved, slightly extended medially, subtruncate above; posterior margin also broadly curved and extended medially, appearing broader than anterior owing to greater height in posterior region. Left valve a little larger than right; valves relatively compressed, greatest convexity posteromedian.

An irregularly shaped portion of posterior end of shell slightly depressed below otherwise smooth surface; about one-fourth from venter depressed area extends abruptly lobate forward; surface of depressed area with obscure nodes and small ridges. Antero-dorsal portion of shell with two obscure shallow depressed areas, separated by a low subvertical ridge. General surface smooth and shiny.

Hinge of right valve consists of an anterior strongly elevated, cleatlike tooth; postero-jacent rounded socket; interterminal furrow; and posterior strongly elevated, slightly curved tooth; anterior end of furrow supported ventrally by a short longitudinal ridge.

Inner lamellae broad anteriorly, narrower ventrally and terminally, slightly sinuate anteromidventrally; line of concrescence and inner margin separated, vestibule broadest anteriorly; radial canals numerous, about 20, and closely spaced anteriorly, bunched ventrally. Adductor muscle scar a slightly anteromedian group of three or four small, closely spaced spots and at least one and perhaps two more-anterior antennal spots.

Length of holotype right valve (Pl. 2, fig. 10b) 0.50 mm, height 0.25 mm, convexity of valve 0.13 mm.

RELATIONSHIPS: The generally smooth shell, shape, and internal structures of the shell of this species are similar to *Cytheretta edwardsi* (Cushman) (1906, p. 382) from Martha's Vineyard, Massachusetts. The particular pattern of depressed posterior surface ornamentation apparently is unique for the new species; although *B. argomega* van den Bold (1963), *B.* species from late Miocene of Trinidad, and *C. sonorensis* Benson and Kaesler (1963) from the Gulf of California are closely similar species.

OCCURRENCE: Recent, Gulf of California, Station 21, depth 32 fathoms, mud bottom; Station 39, depth 21 fathoms, mud bottom; Station 77, depth 3 fathoms, sand bottom; Station 86, depth 30 fathoms, sandy mud bottom; Station 126, depth 20 fathoms, sandy mud bottom; Station 144, depth 75 fathoms, muddy sand bottom; Station 194, depth 75 fathoms, muddy sand bottom; Station 195, depth 75 fathoms, sandy mud bottom.

NUMBER OF SPECIMENS STUDIED: 10

Basslerites sp.
(Pl. 8, fig. 13)

Shell subovate in side view, highest medially; dorsal margin gently convex, sinuous posteriorly due to posterior cardinal projection; ventral margin slightly convex; anterior margin broadly curved, slightly extended below; posterior margin also broadly curved, extended above, subtruncate below. Valve moderately convex, greatest convexity posterior to middle. Left valve larger than right judged from overlap relationships. Surface very finely pitted and with low rim along free margin.

Hinge of left valve consists of anterior deep socket and posterojacent high tooth; interterminal faintly crenulate bar with dorsally adjacent accommodation groove and posterior deep, somewhat elongate socket; inner lamellae of moderate width; line of concrescence and inner margin separated anteriorly, nearly coincident elsewhere; radial canals fairly numerous (about 25) anteriorly, fewer posteriorly, and still fewer ventrally; canals occur at different levels in shell anteriorly; normal canals widely spaced, not coinciding with surface pits. Muscle scar an anteromedian vertical row of three spots and an additional spot anterior to dorsal end of main group.

Length of figured left valve 1.10 mm, height 0.63 mm, convexity of valve 0.50 mm.

REMARKS: The outline, hingement, and marginal structures of this form relate it to *Basslerites* Howe. The nearly smooth, finely pitted surface and posterodorsal projection of margin are unlike other species of *Basslerites;* but the species of this genus are too variable to allow classification on only one left valve.

OCCURRENCE: Recent, Gulf of California, Station 21, depth 32 fathoms, mud bottom.
NUMBER OF SPECIMENS STUDIED: 1

Family LIMNOCYTHERIDAE Klie, 1938
Genus *Limnocythere* Brady, 1868

Limnocythere sanctipatricii Brady and Robertson
(Fig. 47b; Pl. 4, fig. 5a–c)

Limnocythere sancti-patricii BRADY AND ROBERTSON, 1869, Ann. Mag. Nat. Hist., ser. 4, v. 3, p. 17, Pl. 18, figs. 8–11, Pl. 21, fig. 4; BRADY, CROSSKEY, AND ROBERTSON, 1874, Post-Tertiary Entomostraca, Palaeontogr. Soc. Mon., p. 174, Pl. 2, figs. 1–3; BRADY AND NORMAN, 1889, Roy. Dublin Soc. Sci. Trans., ser. 2, v. 4, p. 171, Pl. 17, figs. 1, 2; SWAIN, 1955, Jour. Paleontology, v. 29, p. 613, Figs. 32a, 38–4, Pl. 60, figs. 1a–f, 2a–c; TRESSLER, Fresh Water Biology, 2nd ed., p. 725, Fig. 28:174

Shell elongate, subovate-subquadrate in side view, highest about one-fourth from anterior end; dorsal margin nearly straight with broadly obtuse cardinal angles; ventral margin slightly sinuous, concave posteromedially; anterior margin broadly curved, truncate above; posterior margin more narrowly curved, extended medially. Valves subequal, compressed. Median sulcus extends from dorsal margin to about one-fourth from venter; sulcus bent posteriorly near dorsum; middle half of valve surface swollen on either side of sulcus; general surface finely and weakly pitted.

Hinge of right valve consists of terminal longitudinally elongate small teeth that fit into small sockets of left valve; posterojacent to anterior tooth is a small triangular socket; interterminal portion of right valve hinge a smooth bar, rabbeted above. Marginal zone broad; line of concrescence and inner margin coincide; radial canals spaced. Muscle scar a vertical row of four closely spaced spots, medially placed; other spots not clearly seen. Female shells relatively smaller and with narrower posterior margins than males, which have flared terminal margin.

Length of figured specimen (Pl. 4, fig. 5a) 0.52 mm, height 0.30 mm, convexity 0.20 mm.

REMARKS: The shape and surface ornamentation of the species are bases for reference to *L. sanctipatricii.*

OCCURRENCE: Recent, Gulf of California, freshwater nearshore Station C-80, frequent.
NUMBER OF SPECIMENS STUDIED: 8

Family LOXOCONCHIDAE Sars, 1925
Genus *Loxoconcha* Sars, 1866

Loxoconcha tamarindoidea Swain sp. nov.
(Fig. 46c; Pl. 2, figs. 5, 13, 15a, b, 21)

Outline of shell subquadrate; dorsum and venter nearly straight, subparallel, and about two-thirds of shell length; anterior margin broadly rounded, subtruncate above; posterior margin also broad but extended and rather abruptly curved above. Valves subequal, left slightly larger than right, overlapping and overreaching along free margins. Valves moderately to strongly convex; females shorter, higher, and more convex medially than males.

Surface of valves deeply and coarsely pitted in middle half, and with finely pitted to nearly smooth or slightly rugose bordering area; ventrally pits are arranged concentrically; two very weak ventromedian diverging, narrow ridges extend from near anterior margin posteriorly to about one-third from anterior end; in some specimens one or both ridges may be absent. Ventromedian valve surface more or less swollen in females, less so in males.

Hinge of left valve consists of anterior barlike tooth, interterminal very faintly crenulate bar, and posterior double socket with intervening small tooth and yoked together dorsally by a small furrow.

Inner lamellae narrow; line of concrescence and inner margin slightly separated terminally; radial canals number about 15 anteriorly; left valve with prominent selvage furrow for reception of right valve edge; selvage discontinuity occurs anteromidventrally.

Length of holotype, a female shell, 0.55 mm, height 0.35 mm, convexity 0.28 mm.

RELATIONSHIPS: The outline and general surface ornamentation of the species are similar to those of *Loxoconcha matagordensis* Swain (1955, p. 629) from the Recent bays of Texas; but the pitting of the shell of that species is finer, and the marginal areas are more rugose than in the present species. Except for surface ornamentation the new species is similar in shape to *L. laevata* (Norman) of the North Atlantic and Mediterranean regions; but the shell of that form is nearly smooth, and the antennae are somewhat more slender and delicate than in the new species.

OCCURRENCE: Recent, Gulf of California, Station 23, depth 7 fathoms, sand bottom; Station 39, depth 21 fathoms, muddy sand bottom; Station 41, depth 45 fathoms, sand bottom; Station 52, depth 25 fathoms, sandy mud bottom; Station 67, depth 4 fathoms, sand bottom; Station 78, depth 7 fathoms, sand bottom; Station 87, depth 7 fathoms, sandy mud bottom; Station 88, depth 8 fathoms, gravel and sand bottom; Station 94, depth 4 fathoms, sand bottom; Station 102, depth 6 fathoms, sand bottom; Station 110, depth 10 fathoms, sand bottom; Station 111, depth 7 fathoms, hard clay bottom; Station 119, depth 31 fathoms, sand bottom; Station 123, depth 5 fathoms, sandy mud bottom; Station 138, depth 17 fathoms, muddy sand bottom; Station 141, depth 3 fathoms, sand bottom; Station 140, depth 15 fathoms, shell and sand bottom; Station 143, depth 10 fathoms, sand bottom; Station 144, depth 75 fathoms, muddy sand bottom; Station 153, depth 18 fathoms, muddy sand bottom; Station 156, depth 7 fathoms, sand bottom; Station 158, depth 17 fathoms, muddy sand bottom; Station 162, depth 13 fathoms, sand bottom; Station 173, depth 220 fathoms, muddy sand bottom; Station 175, depth 7.5 fathoms, sand bottom; Station 179, depth 488 fathoms, mud bottom; Station 182, depth 6.7 fathoms, sand bottom; Station 187, depth 13 fathoms, muddy sand bottom; Station 189, depth 10 fathoms, sand bottom; Station 197, depth 28 fathoms, sandy mud bottom; Station 201, depth 13 fathoms, sandy mud bottom; Station 213, depth 8 fathoms, sand bottom; Station 217, depth 15 fathoms, sandy mud bottom.

NUMBER OF SPECIMENS STUDIED: 25 +

Loxoconcha lenticulata LeRoy
(Fig. 54a; Pl. 2, fig. 14)

Loxoconcha lenticulata LeRoy, 1943, Jour. Paleontology, v. 17, p. 360, Figs. 2f, g, Pl. 60, figs. 19–23, Pl. 61, figs. 24–26, Pl. 62, figs. 13, 14; Benson, 1959, Kansas Univ. Paleont. Contr., Arthropoda, art. 1; p. 51, Pl. 4, figs. 3a–d, Pl. 8, figs. 9, 10

Shell subovate in side view, highest medially; dorsal margin strongly convex, anterior slope steeper than posterior; ventral margin slightly convex, straightened anteriorly; anterior margin rather narrowly curved, extended below; posterior margin broadly and nearly uniformly curved. Valves compressed, greatest convexity median. General surface finely and weakly punctate; in free marginal zone a few weak ridges trend parallel to margin.

Hinge of left valve consists of an anterior beadlike tooth with small sockets on either side, an interminal crenulate bar, and a posterior double socket separated by a tooth and yoke-furrow characteristic of genus. Inner lamellae broad, line of concrescence and inner margin slightly separated terminally; radial canals number about 12 terminally. Muscle scar not seen.

Length of figured left valve 0.47 mm, height 0.32 mm, convexity of valve 0.13 mm.

Remarks: The subovate form, strongly arched dorsum, and weak surface pitting distinguish this species from other loxoconchids in the collection.

Occurrence: Recent Gulf of California, Station 21, depth 32 fathoms, mud bottom; Station 143, depth 10 fathoms, sand bottom; previously recorded living from San Diego, Santa Catalina Island, and Monterey Bay and from Pliocene and Pleistocene deposits in California (LeRoy, 1943; Rothwell, 1944), as well as from the Ensenada area, Baja California (Benson, 1959).

Number of Specimens Studied: 4

Loxoconcha? emaciata Swain sp. nov.
(Fig. 48c; Pl. 9, figs. 18a, b)

Shell subquadrate to subtrapezoidal in side view, highest medially; dorsal margin nearly straight to slightly concave, about two-thirds shell length, with broadly obtuse cardinal marginal bends of which the posterior forms the larger angle; ventral margin nearly straight to slightly convex and about same length as dorsum; anterior margin broadly curved, extended near ventral marginal bend; posterior margin also broad but with blunt caudal extension dorsomedially. Valves subequal, compressed, greatest convexity median in position.

Species dimorphic, presumed males more elongate and slightly less convex than presumed females.

Dorsal edge of each valve with prominent, narrow ridge that extends flangelike beyond hinge surface. Ventral margin has low, narrow rim; and terminal margins have fainter rims. Valve surface bears several narrow, strongly elevated, mostly longitudinal ridges as follows: a slightly dorsomedian ridge that begins near anterior margin and terminates posteriad of midlength and has several spurs from its flanks; a slightly ventromedian ridge that begins near anterior margin and terminates anteriad of midlength, has an oblique handlelike ridge across its anterior end, and connects with more dorsal ridge by means of a zig-zag spur from its posterior end; a long subventral oblique ridge, which rises about one-sixth from anterior end and terminates near midheight one-sixth from posterior end, has three ventrally projecting spurs in posterior half; a short ridge occurs ventral to midportion of preceding ridges; Posterodorsally a V-shaped ridge points toward posterodorsal cardinal angle; a few nodes scattered between pits; spurlike extensions from main ridges form an incomplete network of hexagonal structures. A small eye tubercle occurs anterodorsally.

Hinge of right valve consists of an anterior small rounded socket and ventrally adjacent tooth, an interterminal groove and a posterior curved elongate tooth; hinge of left

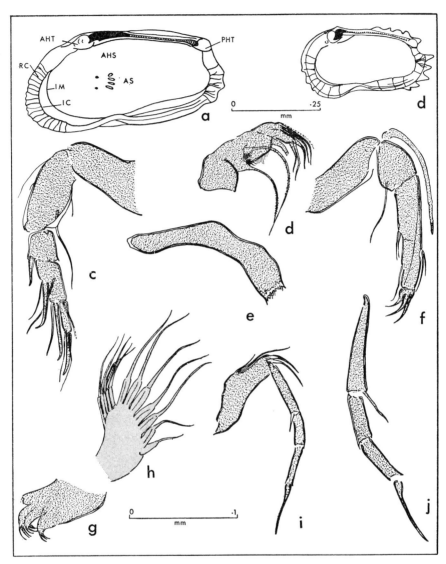

Figure 55. Puriana pacifica *Benson, Scammon Lagoon, Baja California.* (a) Interior of right valve; (b) Interior of immature right valve; (c) Antennule; (d) Palp of mandible; (e) Coxa of Mandible; (f) Antenna; (g) Maxilla; (h) Respiratory lobe of maxilla; (i) First thoracic leg; (j) Part of second thoracic leg

valve consists of an anterior bent tooth enclosing a small socket ventrally, an interterminal faintly crenulate bar, and a posterior socket. Inner lamellae broad along entire free margins; line of concrescence and inner margin nearly coincide; radial canals few and widely spaced. Muscle scar a slightly anteromedian vertical row of four closely spaced spots and two more-anterior spots.

Length of holotype, a male?, right valve 0.48 mm, height 0.28 mm, convexity of valve 0.13 mm. Length of female? paratype left valve 0.43 mm, height 0.28 mm, convexity of valve 0.15 mm.

RELATIONSHIPS: The shape, hingement, musculature, broad inner lamellae, and caudal process ally the species to *Loxoconcha* Sars. The pattern of narrow surface ridges which forms roughly hexagonal "benzenoid" structures is apparently unique. *Loxoconcha lapidiscola* Hartmann (1959b, p. 223) from El Salvador is similar to the present form, but the shell ornamentation is slightly different. Hartmann's species and the present one are probably congeneric and may be a new genus.

OCCURRENCE: Recent, Gulf of California, Station 189, depth 10 fathoms, sand bottom.

NUMBER OF SPECIMENS STUDIED: 2

Genus *Cytheromorpha* Hirschmann, 1909

Cytheromorpha sp. aff. *C. warneri* Howe and Spurgeon
(Pl. 9, fig. 15)

Shell elongate-subquadrate in side view, highest anteromedially; dorsal margin nearly straight to gently convex with slight notch at posterior end; ventral margin slightly concave; anterior margin broadly curved, slightly extended below; posterior margin narrower, strongly extended above, truncate to slightly concave below. Left valve larger than right and extends beyond right along dorsal, ventral, and posterior margins. Valves not strongly convex, greatest convexity posteromedian.

Anterodorsal surface of valves with short, weak, oblique sulcus that lies ventral to eye tubercle; general surface finely pitted; pits arranged in concentric rows anteriorly and ventrally.

Internal structures of shell mostly not observed. Muscle scar a median vertical row of three or four spots, perhaps with one or more anterior antennal spots.

Length of figured specimen 0.54 mm, height 0.27 mm, convexity 0.22 mm.

REMARKS: This form is similar to *Cytheromorpha warneri* Howe and Spurgeon (in Howe and others, 1935, p. 11) from the Miocene of Florida in shape but is more finely pitted than that species. Too little information is available on the internal shell structure of the present form to enable it to be classified more definitely.

OCCURRENCE: Recent, Gulf of California, Station 192, depth 262 fathoms, mud bottom.

NUMBER OF SPECIMENS STUDIED: 1

Genus *Loxocorniculum* Benson and Coleman, 1963

Loxocorniculum sculptoides Swain sp. nov.
(Fig. 57; Pl. 2, fig. 20)

Shell subovate in side view, highest medially; dorsal margin strongly arched with steeper anterior than posterior slope; ventral margin slightly sinuous, concave antero-medially; anterior margin rounded, strongly extended below; posterior margin more broadly curved than anterior, extended and slightly angulated above, truncated dorsad of angulation.

General surface of valve, except smooth, narrow terminal borders, ornamented by large to small pits, coarser near valve middle, finer near margins, arranged in a pattern roughly parallel to margins owing to a reticulate arrangement of ridgelike elevations separating pits; pits small and weak in central portion of valve; posterodorsal cardinal area with prominent node that extends beyond valve margin; reticulating ridges are gathered to node in posterior part of valve; two weak ridges lie perpendicular to anterior margin, one at midheight, the other more ventrally located.

Hinge of left valve formed of an anterior elongate, slightly crenulate socket, postero-jacent tooth, interterminal bar and dorsally adjacent narrow accommodation groove, and posterior double socket separated by a small tooth and yoked together by a furrow dorsal to tooth. Hinge of right valve is antithesis of left. Inner lamellae fairly broad; line of concrescence and inner margin nearly coincide; radial canals few and widely spaced, nearly straight.

Antennule consists of six podomeres, first two broad, the others much narrower; second podomere with two midanterior setae, finely hairy anterior margin, and distal posterior seta; fifth podomere with two long swimming setae; and ultimate podomere with three long swimming setae.

Antenna composed of four broad podomeres, the last two nearly fused; second podomere much shorter than basis; fourth podomere long, finely hairy on posterior margin and bearing three strong claws directly on its distal edge; exopodite extends to ends of distal claws.

Mandible with about seven long teeth on cutting edge; palp with four poorly defined segments; the second bears two strong, ventral, distal, clawlike setae and two additional setae; third segment has one ventral and two dorsal strong setae; and ultimate segment bears three terminal clawlike setae.

Protopodite of maxilla composed of three masticatory setaceous lobes; endopodite palp rudely segmented and provided with three long setae from proximal segment; respiratory plate has about 15 long, unfeathered rays.

First thoracic leg three-segmented beyond basis; second and third legs four-segmented; distal edge of basis with two setae in second and third legs, one seta in first leg.

Furca small and three-segmented, each bearing clawlike inner or terminal setae.

Length of holotype left valve 0.55 mm, height 0.37 mm, convexity of valve 0.17 mm.

RELATIONSHIPS: The shape, hingement, and posterodorsal node relate the species to *Loxocorniculum* Benson and Coleman. The shape and node are similar to features of *Loxoconcha sculpta* Brady (1868a, p. 140), but that species is more coarsely pitted and lacks the minor features of surface ornamentation of the present form.

OCCURRENCE: Recent, Gulf of California, Station 67, rare.

NUMBER OF SPECIMENS STUDIED: 3 (1 living)

Genus *Pteroloxa* Swain, 1963

Pteroloxa guaymasensis Swain sp. nov.
(Pl. 8, fig. 3)

Shell subquadrate in side view, highest anteromedially; dorsal margin nearly straight, about four-fifths of shell length with obtuse cardinal angles; ventral margin gently convex; anterior margin broadly curved, extended medially; posterior margin more narrowly curved, extended and angulated above. Valves moderately convex, greatest convexity posteroventral.

Surface ornamented by an oblique, narrow, somewhat irregular ridge that extends from middle of anterior margin nearly to posteroventral margin where it curves dorsally subparallel to posterior margin to a point below posterior cardinal angle from whence it bends forward along dorsum for a short distance and ends against dorsal margin; a narrow ridge parallels dorsal margin; another narrow ridge extends ventrally from anterior part of dorsum to midheight, then turns abruptly toward posterior margin as a median ridge; ventral ridge is joined at midlength by another more ventral ridge that rises near anteroventral marginal bend; a short longitudinal ridge lies between ventral and median ridges posteromedially; an eye tubercle through which passes a short subvertical ridge occurs anterodorsally; general surface coarsely reticulate.

Hinge of left valve consists of an anterior curved socket on either side of which is a small tooth, an interterminal bar formed of valve edge, and a posterior socket on either side of which occurs a small, beadlike tooth. Inner lamellae relatively narrow; line of concrescence and inner margin apparently coincide. Radial canals and muscle scar not observed.

Length of holotype left valve 0.36 mm, height 0.22 mm, convexity of valve 0.12 mm.

RELATIONSHIPS: The general shape, hingement, and ventral oblique ridge are features that ally this species with *Pteroloxa* Swain (1963, p. 820). The particular pattern of surface ornamentation is apparently unique for this species.

OCCURRENCE: Recent, Gulf of California, Station 130, depth 62 fathoms, sandy mud bottom (holotype); also from Station 21, depth 32 fathoms, mud bottom.
NUMBER OF SPECIMENS STUDIED: 3

Family PARADOXOSTOMATIDAE Brady and Norman, 1889
Subfamily PARADOXOSTOMATINAE Brady and Norman, 1889
Genus *Paradoxostoma* Fischer, 1855

Paradoxostoma cf. *hodgei* Brady
(Pl. 2, fig. 19)

Paradoxostoma hodgei BRADY, 1870, Nat. Hist. Northumberland and Durham Trans., v. 3, p. 371, Pl. 12, figs. 12, 13; Brady and Norman, 1889, Roy. Dublin Soc. Sci. Trans., v. 4, p. 235, Pl. 21, figs. 7, 8

Shell elongate, sublanceolate-reniform in side view, highest medially; dorsal margin convex, sloping more or less uniformly on either side of position of greatest height; ventral margin somewhat sinusoidal, concave anteromedially; anterior margin narrowly rounded, strongly extended below; posterior margin somewhat less narrowly rounded, extended medially. Valves subequal, convexity low, most convexity medially. Surface smooth.

Hinge surface of right valve consists of a weak rabbet furrow that apparently slightly overlaps hinge margin of left valve; inner lamellae very broad anteriorly and posteroventrally; line of concrescence and inner margin widely separated in those areas; radial canals few and widely spaced; adductor muscle scar consists of a vertical row of three subparallel, irregular, but generally elongate spots, together with a more-anterior, large, rounded antennal spot.

Length of figured right valve 0.46 mm, height 0.20 mm, convexity of valve 0.09 mm.

REMARKS: The extreme elongation and narrow ends of this form are suggestive of *Xiphichilus* Brady; but it is considerably less acuminate than *X. tenuissima* Norman, the type species. It closely resembles *Paradoxostoma hodgei* Brady and is tentatively referred to that species.

OCCURRENCE: Recent, Gulf of California, Station 5, depth 1,572 fathoms, mud bottom; Station 143, depth 10 fathoms, sand bottom; Station 162, depth 13 fathoms, sand bottom; Station 175, depth 7.5 fathoms, sand bottom.
NUMBER OF SPECIMENS STUDIED: 6

Paradoxostoma micropunctata Swain sp. nov.
(Fig. 54b; Pl. 2, fig. 18)

Shell sublanceolate in side view, highest a little posterior to midlength; dorsal margin moderately convex, sinuous, and slightly concave along posterior slope; ventral margin sinuous, slightly concave anteriorly, and somewhat convex posteriorly; anterior margin narrowly curved, extended ventral to midheight; posterior margin bluntly pointed, extended medially. Valves moderately convex, greatest convexity median. Surface minutely punctate; in addition to punctae, dorsal part of valve weakly marked with irregular ridges and depressions.

Hinge of right valve consists of an anterior strongly elevated, pointed tooth set on interior valve surface at dorsal end of inner lamella; an interterminal weak rabbet groove lying just ventrad of valve edge; and a posterior faint socket-depression. Inner lamella broad, widest terminally; line of concrescence and inner margin separate, strongly sinuous anteroventrally, and scalloped anteroventrally and posteroventrally where pore canals emerge; radial canals relatively few and widely spaced around entire periphery. Muscle scar a slightly anteromedian vertical row of four closely spaced spots, a fairly large antennal scar anterior to ventral end of main group, and possibly a second more dorsal antennal scar.

Length of right valve 0.47 mm, height 0.23 mm, convexity of valve 0.10 mm.

RELATIONSHIPS: The shape, hingement, and marginal structures of this species relate it to *Paradoxostoma*. The surface ornamentation is unlike other species of the genus known to the author.

OCCURRENCE: Recent, Gulf of California, Station 102, depth 6 fathoms, sand bottom.

NUMBER OF SPECIMENS STUDIED: 2

Genus *Cytherois* Müller, 1884

Cytherois cf. *fischeri* (Sars)
(Pl. 9, figs. 4a, b)

Paradoxostoma fischeri SARS, 1866, Oversigt af Norges marine Ostracoder, p. 96; BRADY, 1870, Nat. Hist. Trans. Northumberland and Durham, v. 3, p. 362, Pl. 12, figs. 1–3; BBADY, CROSSKEY, AND ROBERTSON, 1874, Post-Tertiary Entomostraca, Palaeontogr. Soc., p. 215, Pl. 16, figs. 23, 24

Cytherois fischeri (Sars). BRADY AND NORMAN, 1889, Roy. Dublin Soc. Sci. Trans., ser. 2, v. 4, p. 228, Pl. 21, figs. 20–22; SARS, 1928, Crustacea of Norway, p. 252, Pl. 114; KLIE, 1938, Tierwelt Deutschl., v. 34, no. 3, p. 221; ELOFSON, 1941, Zool. Bidrag fran Uppsala, v. 19, p. 347; WAGNER, 1957, Ostracodes Quat. Rec. Pays-Bas, et leur utilisation dans l'etude geologique des depots Holocene, Mouton Co., The Hague, p. 99, Pl. 49

Shell elongate-sublanceolate, highest medially to posteromedially; dorsal margin gently convex; ventral margin somewhat sinuous, slightly concave anteromedially; anterior margin narrowly rounded, strongly extended below; posterior margin somewhat more broadly rounded, strongly extended medially. Valves compressed, greatest convexity median. Shell surface smooth.

Hinge margin of left valve consists of a slightly extended ridge formed of valve edge and with faint notches at either end of ridge. Inner lamellae very broad; line of concrescence and inner margin widely separated; radial canals short and rather widely spaced; adductor muscle scar an oblique anteromedian row of three or four closely spaced spots, perhaps one or two additional more-anterior antennal spots, together with several more-dorsal diductor muscle spots.

Length of figured left valve specimen 0.53 mm, height 0.20 mm, convexity of valve 0.83 mm.

REMARKS: The outline and internal shell structures of these forms are closely similar to *Cytherois fischeri*, but they are perhaps somewhat more elongate than is typical for the species.

OCCURRENCE: Recent, Gulf of California, Station 179, depth 488 fathoms, mud bottom.

NUMBER OF SPECIMENS STUDIED: 2

Genus *Paracytherois* Müller, 1894

Paracytherois? *perspicilla* (Benson and Kaesler)
(Pl. 9, fig. 5)

Parakrithella perspicilla BENSON AND KAESLER, 1963, Kansas Univ. Paleont. Cont., Arthropoda, art. 3, p. 20, Fig. 9; Pl. 2, figs. 7, 8

Shell subovate, almond-shaped in side view, highest posteromedially; dorsal margin strongly convex; ventral margin sinuous, concave posteromedially; anterior margin broadly curved, strongly extended below; posterior margin bluntly pointed, extended medially. Convexity of valves low, greatest convexity slightly posteromedian. Surface smooth. Left valve slightly larger than right, overlapping right along free margins. A weak dorsomedian oblique depression lies ventral to eye spot.

Hingement not seen in specimens at hand. Inner lamellae broad; line of concrescence and inner margin widely separated; anterior end with well-defined pocketlike vestibule formed by sinuosity of line of concrescence; radial canals short and rather widely spaced. Muscle scar not clearly seen.

Length of figured specimen 0.60 mm, height 0.32 mm, convexity of shell 0.22 mm

REMARKS: The shape and observed internal shell structures of this form resemble those of *P.?perspicilla* (Benson and Kaesler, 1963, p. 20). The generic status of the species is somewhat questionable, but the line of concrescence and pore canals more nearly resemble *Paracytherois* than *Parakrithella*.

OCCURRENCE: Recent, Gulf of California, Station 77, depth 3 fathoms, sand bottom.

NUMBER OF SPECIMENS STUDIED: 3

Genus *Sclerochilus* Sars, 1866

Sclerochilus? contortellus Swain sp. nov.
(Pl. 9, fig. 6)

Shell elongate-sublanceolate-subreniform in side view, highest about one-third from posterior end; dorsal margin moderately convex; ventral margin concave anteromedially; anterior margin narrowly rounded, extended below; posterior margin more broadly rounded, extended medially. Left valve slightly larger than and extends beyond margin of right valve. Valves more or less compressed, greatest convexity median. Surface smooth.

Hinge consists of simple groove in edge of left valve for reception of edge of right valve. Inner lamellae very broad, especially anteriorly; line of concrescence and inner margin widely separated; radial canals relatively short, about 18 to 20 anteriorly, becoming sparser ventrally and again numerous posteriorly; line of concrescence fairly smooth. Muscle scar not clearly seen; it lies anteromedially and is formed of an oblique row of three or four elongate spots.

Antenna with distal segment subdivided, only 2 apical claws observed; mandible with cutting edge broad and nearly at right angles to margins of palp, rather than strongly oblique as is typical of genus, about six bifid teeth; maxilla with distal segment short and setose; endopod two-jointed with many apical setae; vibratory palp rounded; first? thoracic leg three-segmented beyond basis.

Length of figured specimen 0.40 mm, height 0.23 mm, convexity 0.17 mm.

RELATIONSHIPS: The elongate reniform outline, smooth surface, and marginal features of the present, apparently mature specimens are very similar to those of *S. contortus* (Norman), a nearly cosmopolitan species; but the shell of the new species is smaller, and the appendages are very different in detail. The mandible and maxilla of the present form are so atypical of *Sclerochilus* as to cast doubt on the generic assignment of the species.

OCCURRENCE: Recent, Gulf of California, Station 41, depth 45 fathoms, sand bottom; Station 53, depth 8 fathoms, sand bottom; Station 142, depth 15 fathoms, sand bottom; Station 144, depth 75 fathoms, muddy sand bottom.

NUMBER OF SPECIMENS STUDIED: 4 (1 living)

Genus *Xiphichilus* Sars, 1866

Xiphichilus tenuissimoides Swain sp. nov.
(Pl. 2, fig. 11; Pl. 9, figs. 14a–c)

Shell elongate-lanceolate-acuminate in side view, highest medially; dorsal margin slightly convex, sloping uniformly from position of greatest height; ventral margin of approximately equal convexity; anterior margin narrowly rounded, strongly extended medially; posterior margin acuminately pointed, also extended medially. Valves subequal, compressed, greatest convexity median. Surface smooth.

Hinge line formed of simple edges of valves. Inner lamellae very broad terminally and ventrally; line of concrescence and inner margin widely separated; line of concrescence scalloped owing to flared inner ends of radial canals; anterior vestibule accentuated by ventral sinuation in line of concrescence about one-sixth from anterior end; radial canals relatively few and widely spaced; about eight occur anteriorly. Adductor muscle scar formed of about four elongate sinuous, oblique spots lying in a compact anteromedian group.

Length of figured left valve 0.74 mm, height 0.88 mm, convexity 0.27 mm.

RELATIONSHIPS: The shape and marginal structures of this species furnish a comparison with *X. tenuissima* (Norman) from the British Isles, but the latter shell is larger than the Gulf of California specimens.

OCCURRENCE: Recent, Gulf of California, Station 39, depth 21 fathoms, muddy sand bottom; Station 153, depth 18 fathoms, muddy sand bottom.

NUMBER OF SPECIMENS STUDIED: 4

Subfamily CYTHEROMATINAE Elofson, 1939

Genus *Cytheroma* Müller, 1894

Cytheroma? sp. aff. *"Microcythere" gibba* Müller

(Pl. 7, fig. 10)

Shell elongate-subelliptical in side view, highest near anterior end; dorsal margin very slightly convex; ventral margin concave anteromedially; anterior margin broadly and nearly uniformly curved; posterior margin more narrowly rounded, extended medially. Valves compressed, greatest convexity median. Surface smooth.

Hinge line of right valve formed of slight terminal projections that presumably fit into weak furrows on left valve (not seen); *i.e.*, a lophodont hinge. Muscle scar a slightly anteromedian vertical row of four closely spaced spots and an additional more-anterior spot that consists of four smaller spots in contact with each other. Inner lamellae broad terminally, especially at anterior end; inner margin and line of concrescence widely separated; line of concrescence very irregular terminally; anteriorly it is formed by the inner terminations of 12 to 15 short sinuous radial canals that have broadly funnel-shaped inner openings; posteriorly, line of concrescence is of 8 to 10 short radial canals.

Length of figured specimen 0.42 mm, height 0.17 mm, convexity of valve 0.08 mm.

REMARKS: The subelliptical outline, marginal structures, and musculature of the present species relate it to *Cytheroma* Müller. It seems close to *Microcythere gibba* Müller (1894, p. 371) in the shape of the anterior portion of the valve, but there is insufficient material in the present collection for definite identification.

OCCURRENCE: Recent, Gulf of California, Station 162, depth 13 fathoms, sand bottom.

NUMBER OF SPECIMENS STUDIED: 2

Genus *Megacythere* Puri, 1960

Megacythere punctocostata Swain sp. nov.

(Fig. 56; Pl. 8, figs. 9a, b)

Shell elongate-subquadrate-subtrapezoidal in side view, highest one-fourth from anterior end; dorsal margin nearly straight to slightly convex, merging gradually with anterior margin but forming a broadly obtuse angle with posterior margin; ventral margin slightly concave; anterior margin broadly curved, somewhat extended below; posterior margin more narrowly curved, extended medially; valves more or less compressed, greatest convexity posteromedian. Valves nearly equal in size, the left slightly larger than right.

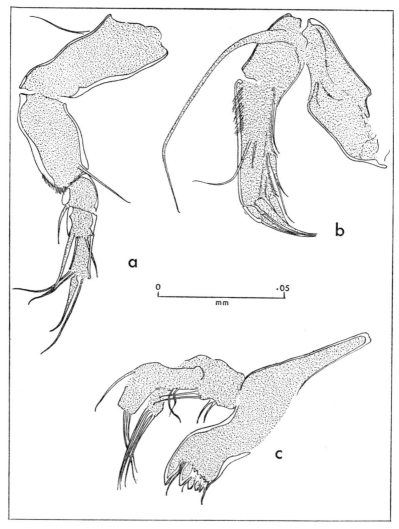

Figure 56. Megacythere punctocostata *Swain sp. nov., Gulf of California, Station 78.*
(a) Antennule; (b) Antenna; (c) Mandible and palp

Valve surfaces with about 10 narrow, longitudinal, low, in part discontinuous and irregular ridges, between which interspaces are densely pitted in one, two, or three rows dependinging on width of interspaces between pits.

Hinge of right valve consists of an anterior socket supported by a cleatlike elevation from interior valve surface, an interterminal furrow, and a posterior small socket; hinge of left valve consists of an anterior small tooth, an interterminal bar formed of valve edge, and a posterior tooth. Inner lamellae very broad anteriorly, narrower posteriorly and ventrally. Line of concrescence and inner margin widely separated anteriorly where concrescence line is strongly scalloped; radial canals anteriorly open along scalloped line of concrescence as funnellike terminations. Adductor muscle scar an anteromedian oblique row of three small, closely spaced spots and one or two additional more-anterior spots. Antennule with three podomeres beyond basis, the latter with a single outer proximal seta; second podomere has a fringe of hairs on outer edge near distal margin and an inner distal seta; third podomere with two outer distal setae; fourth podomere bears one outer and two inner distal setae; ultimate podomere has four terminal setae, one of which is thicker and more clawlike than others.

Antenna three-segmented; second podomere has an inner distal seta; third podomere long, apparently consisting of two or three fused segments; midsection with about four setae of variable length; two terminal claws strongly developed.

Mandible has five pairs of teeth on cutting margin; these become progressively shorter and smaller from outer to inner margin; palp biramous beyond first segment, each ramus with terminal setae, and outer ramus has median seta; first segment of palp bears four setae on inner side.

Other appendages not well preserved in specimens at hand.

Length of right valve of holotype 0.38 mm, height 0.18 mm, convexity 0.07 mm; length of left valve of holotype 0.38 mm, height 0.14 mm, convexity 0.07 mm.

RELATIONSHIPS: The surface ornamentation, shape, hingement, and other features of this species are similar to those of *Megacythere johnsoni* (Mincher, 1941, p. 641) from the later Tertiary and Recent of the Gulf of Mexico region; but the longitudinal ridges are considerably narrower than in *johnsoni*, and pitted interspaces between the ridges are not recorded in *johnsoni*. The forms described as *M. johnsoni* (Mincher) by Benson and Kaesler (1963, p. 28) and as *Paracytheroma costata* Hartmann (1957, p. 158) from Baja California and El Salvador, respectively, are also similar to the present species but lack the interridge pits.

OCCURRENCE: Recent, Gulf of California, Station 21, depth 32 fathoms, mud bottom; Station 39, depth 21 fathoms, muddy sand bottom; Station 78, depth 10 fathoms, sand bottom; Station 87, depth 7 fathoms, sandy mud bottom; Station 112, depth 34 fathoms, hard clay bottom; Station 123, depth 5 fathoms, sandy mud bottom; Station 179, depth 488 fathoms, mud bottom; Station 195, depth 75 fathoms, sandy mud bottom; Station 217, depth 15 fathoms, sandy mud bottom.

NUMBER OF SPECIMENS STUDIED: 13 (1 living)

Genus *Pellucistoma* Coryell and Fields, 1937

Pellucistoma scrippsi Benson
(Pl. 2, fig. 17)

Pellucistoma scrippsi BENSON, 1959, Kansas Univ. Paleont. Contr. Arthropoda, art. 1, p. 58, Pl. 5, figs. 4a, b, Pl. 9, fig. 5c; BENSON AND KAESLER, 1963, ibid., art. 3, p. 28, Fig. 17; Pl. 2, figs. 3, 4

Shell sublanceolate in side view, highest slightly posteromedially; dorsal margin moderately convex; ventral margin sinuous, concave anteromedially; anterior margin rounded, strongly extended below, and sharply curved at posteroventral marginal bend; posterior margin acuminate, strongly extended above as a blunt caudal process. Valves subequal, left slightly larger than right; valves not strongly convex, greatest thickness of capapace median. Surface smooth, but with small eye tubercle elevation anterodorsally.

Hinge of left valve a long, smooth ridge slightly enlarged at anterior end; hinge surface of right valve weakly furrowed and with enlargement at anterior end for reception of hinge bar of left valve. Inner lamellae broad along entire free margin; line of concrescence strongly scalloped and widely separated from inner margin in pocketlike anterior area; also somewhat scalloped posteroventrally where a small, irregular vestibule occurs; elsewhere line of concrescence and inner margin nearly coincide; radial canals number about 12 anteriorly, where they are in part branching and are fewer and more widely spaced ventrally and posteriorly. Muscle scar an anteromedian vertical row of four small spots and two additional more-anterior antennal spots.

Length of figured shell 0.48 mm, height 0.27 mm, convexity 0.20 mm.

REMARKS: The scalloped line of concrescence and its configuration are characteristic of *Pellucistoma*. The broad inner lamellae are more suggestive of *Paradoxostoma* than of *Pellucistoma*, in which the inner lamellae are typically narrow. The present specimens, although somewhat uncertain generically, appear to be identical with *P. scrippsi* Benson.

OCCURRENCE: Recent, Gulf of California, Station 21, depth 32 fathoms, mud bottom; Station 87, depth 7 fathoms, sandy mud bottom; Station 102, depth 6 fathoms, sand bottom; Station 123, depth 5 fathoms, sandy mud bottom. Benson recorded this species from localities on the Pacific coast of Baja California and from the Gulf of California along the Sonora Coast, Mexico.

NUMBER OF SPECIMENS STUDIED: 6

Family TRACHYLEBERIDIDAE Sylvester-Bradley, 1948
Genus *Cativella* Coryell and Fields, 1937

Cativella dispar Hartmann
(Fig. 36b; Pl. 3, figs. 2a, b)

Cativella dispar Hartmann, 1959b, Kieler Meeresforschungen, v. 15, p. 234, 235, Figs. 168–172

Cativella cf. *dispar* Hartmann. BENSON AND KAESLER, 1963, Kansas Univ. Paleont. Contr., Arthropoda, art. 3, p. 29, Fig. 18; Pl. 3, figs. 5, 6

Shell subquadrate-subpyriform in side view, highest one-fourth from anterior end; dorsal and ventral margins slightly convex; anterior margin broadly curved, bearing six to eight short, thick spines; posterior margin much narrower, acuminately extended, with five blunt spines below, and is markedly concave above; left valve slightly larger than right, extending beyond right in anterior cardinal area. Valves moderately convex, greatest convexity in ventromedian part of shell.

Dorsal, anterior, and ventral margins with strongly elevated, sharp-crested ridges, from inner flanks of which project numerous spurs; rounded eye tubercle anterodorsally on inner flank of ridge. Long, narrow, strongly elevated median ridge extends for four-fifths of valve length and short spurs project from flanks of ridge; ventral longitudinal ridge shorter than median ridge, terminates posteriorly in spinelike elevation; spurs occur on flanks of ridge; perforations extend through median ridge and at several places along marginal ridge between spurs; latter are external expressions of air chambers in ridges that probably are flotational features.

Hinge of right valve comprises an anterior high curved tooth, notched on ventral side; posterojacent rounded socket; interterminal, weakly crenulate narrow groove; and posterior high curved tooth, also notched on ventral side. Inner lamellae moderately broad, line of concrescence and inner margin not separated; radial canals numerous and closely but irregularly spaced terminally, fewer ventrally. Adductor muscle scar a slightly anteromedian vertical row of three spots lying at posterior edge of a subcentral circular depressed area, one more-anterior antennal scar, and possibly one mandibular scar.

Length of a figured specimen (Pl. 3, fig. 12a) 0.65 mm, height 0.37 mm, convexity of valves 0.33 mm.

REMARKS: *Cativella dispar* Hartmann is closely similar to *Pterygocythereis delicata* (Coryell and Fields) in shape and general surface ornamentation, but the latter does not have a median ridge. *P. translucens* Crouch has the posterior margin more completely spinose, as described by Crouch (1949, p. 597). *C. unitaria* sp. nov. is also similar to *C. dispar* but has shorter flanking spurs than in *C. unitaria*, in which they tend to extend across entire interspace between longitudinal ridges. There are subsidiary nodes on the spurs in *C. unitaria* that are not present in *C. dispar*.

OCCURRENCE: Recent, Gulf of California, Station 41, depth 45 fathoms, sand bottom;

Station 87, depth 7 fathoms, sandy mud bottom; Station 88, depth 8 fathoms, gravel and sand bottom; Station 102, depth 6 fathoms, sand bottom; Station 119, depth 31 fathoms, sand bottom; Station 158, depth 17 fathoms, muddy sand bottom; Station 197, depth 28 fathoms, sandy mud bottom; Station 204, depth 40 fathoms, muddy sand bottom.

NUMBER OF SPECIMENS STUDIED: 12

Cativella unitaria Swain sp. nov.
(Pl. 3, fig. 15)

Shell subquadrate-subpyriform in side view, highest one-fourth from anterior end; dorsal and ventral margins gently convex, converging slightly in posterior direction; anterior margin broadly rounded, somewhat extended below, bearing about 12 spines, several of which have thickened, cleatlike terminations; posterior margin strongly and acuminately extended a little ventral to midheight, strongly concave above, and with six long to short spines below. Valves subequal, left slightly larger; valves moderately convex, greatest convexity posteromedian.

Dorsal, anterior, and ventral margins of valve with strongly elevated, sharp-crested ridge; anterodorsally, ridge is arched and includes rounded glassy eye tubercle; spurlike ridges extend perpendicularly from both sides of ridge; those on marginal side and on inner side of ventral portion slope steeply to valve edge; those on inner side of dorsum and anterior are longer, connect for most part with similar spurs from median longitudinal ridge, and are marked by inconspicuous low nodes at several of those junctions; spurs are exterior expressions of small air chambers along ridge. Median longitudinal ridge with similar spurs and air chambers, occupies middle three-fourths of valve, curves toward dorsum in posterior part. Ventral submarginal longitudinal ridge, somewhat shorter than median ridge, has spurs on both sides; those along inner side connect with spurs of median ridge, junctions generally marked by nodes; posterior end of ventral ridge strongly elevated as a spine.

Hinge of right valve with anterior high tooth notched on ventral side; posterojacent socket; narrow, faintly crenulate interterminal groove; and posterior high tooth. Inner lamellae of moderate width but apparently do not continue along dorsal side of posterior margin; line of concrescence and inner margin nearly coincide; radial canals numerous but irregularly spaced. Muscle scar not observed.

Length of figured right valve 0.57 mm, height 0.30 mm, convexity of valve 0.17 mm.

RELATIONSHIPS: The shape and general surface ornamentation of this species are like *C. dispar* Hartmann, but this species has longer spurs from longitudinal dorsal median and ventromedian ridges that does that species. The name of the new species refers to the uniting of the spurs from the longitudinal ridges.

OCCURRENCE: Recent, Gulf of California, Station 21, depth 32 fathoms, mud bottom; Station 39, depth 21 fathoms, muddy sand bottom; Station 41, depth 45 fathoms, sand bottom; Station 52, depth 25 fathoms, sandy mud bottom; Station 87, depth 7 fathoms, sandy mud bottom; Station 94, depth 4 fathoms, sand botom; Station 100, depth 38 fathoms, gravel and sand bottom; Station 110, depth 10 fathoms, sand bottom; Station 111, depth 7 fathoms, hard clay bottom; Station 112, depth 34 fathoms, hard clay bottom; Station 123, depth 5 fathoms, sandy mud bottom; Station 126, depth 20 fathoms, sandy mud bottom; Station 130, depth 62 fathoms, sandy mud bottom; Station 138, depth 17 fathoms, muddy sand bottom; Station 143, depth 10 fathoms, sand bottom; Station 153, depth 18 fathoms, muddy sand bottom; Station 179, depth 488 fathoms, mud bottom; Station 204, depth 40 fathoms, muddy sand bottom; Station 216, depth 18 fathoms, sandy mud bottom; Station 217, depth 15 fathoms, sandy mud bottom.

NUMBER OF SPECIMENS STUDIED: 25 +

Genus *Costa* Neviani, 1928

Costa? cf. *variabilocostata seminuda* van den Bold
(Pl. 3, fig. 14)

Costa variabilocostata seminuda VAN DEN BOLD, 1958, Micropaleontology, v. 4, p. 405, Pl 3, figs. 1a, b

Shell elongate-subpyriform in side view, highest about one-fifth from anterior end; dorsal margin nearly straight to slightly concave medially with obtuse cardinal marginal bends, of which anterior is more sharply curved than posterior; ventral margin somewhat sinuous posteriorly owing to alae, otherwise gently convex, converging with dorsum toward posterior; anterior margin broadly and nearly uniformly convex, slightly extended below; posterior margin with posteroventral subcaudate, flangelike extension that bears three or four small, short spines. Valves subequal, left somewhat larger than right; shell compressed, greatest convexity posteromedian.

Anterior margin with low, narrow, smooth rim that continues along venter to end of ala, about one-fourth from posterior end; anterodorsal eye tubercle an elongate marginal elevation, posterior to which a dorsal marginal ridge extends down posterior margin to below midheight; low, rounded anteromedian swelling has a short longitudinal ridge posterior to it; a submarginal ventral longitudinal ridge in middle three-fifths of shell; general surface densely and finely pitted together with a superimposed coarse, weak, reticulate network of small ridges.

Hinge of immature left valve consists of anterior elongate socket, interterminal bar, and posterior socket. Other internal structures not observed in specimens at hand.

Length of figured right valve 0.54 mm, height 0.29 mm, convexity 0.13 mm.

REMARKS: Although poorly preserved, the present specimens have the shape and external ornamentation of *Costa seminuda* van den Bold. The internal shell characters were not sufficiently well preserved to permit definite identification.

OCCURRENCE: Recent, Gulf of California, Station 41, depth 45 fathoms, sand bottom; Station 144, depth 90 fathoms, muddy sand bottom; Station 179, depth 448 fathoms, mud bottom; Station 216, depth 18 fathoms, sandy mud bottom. The subspecies was described from the Lower Miocene Brasso Formation of Trinidad (van den Bold, 1958, p. 405).

NUMBER OF SPECIMENS STUDIED: 7

Costa? *sanfelipensis* Swain sp. nov.
(Pl. 9, fig. 13)

Shell subquadrate-sublanceolate in side view, highest about one-fourth from anterior end; dorsal margin nearly straight to slightly convex; ventral margin nearly straight, converging posteriorly toward dorsum; anterior margin broadly and uniformly curved, fringed with small spines; posterior margin narrower, strongly extended below, truncate above, with several small spines below. Valves compressed, greatest convexity posteromedian.

Dorsal margin with low, irregular marginal ridge posterior to small glassy eye tubercle; anterior margin with submarginal double ridge, each part of which is narrow crested; small crossbars connect two parts of ridge; ventral margin with narrow ridge that passes around posterior margin into a somewhat broader ridge; median longitudinal ridge rises in anteromedian tubercle about two-fifths from anterior end, trends obliquely toward posterodorsal end of hinge, near which it broadens and ends a short spur to dorsal margin and a second spur posteroventrally; ventromedially a longitudinal narrow ridge occupies middle two-thirds of venter; general surface coarsely reticulate.

Hinge of right valve consists of anterior small, rounded tooth; posterojacent comma-shaped socket; interterminal groove; and posterior curved tooth. Inner lamellae of moderate width; line of concrescence and inner margin slightly separated terminally; radial canals numerous and closely spaced terminally, but somewhat irregular. Muscle scar not observed.

Length of holotype right valve 0.52 mm, height 0.27 mm, convexity of valve 0.10 mm.

RELATIONSHIPS: This form is more elongate, has a stronger and more continuous median longitudinal ridge, and coarser surface reticulation of the valve than *Costa? cf. variabilocostata seminuda* van den Bold of this paper.

NUMBER OF SPECIMENS STUDIED: 3

Genus *Puriana* Coryell and Fields, 1953

Puriana pacifica Benson
(Figs. 55a–j; Pl. 3, figs. 1a–c; Pl. 6, figs. 4a–c)

Puriana pacifica Benson, 1959, Kansas Univ. Paleont. Contr., Arthropoda, art. 1, p. 60, Fig. 61, Pl. 5, figs. 5a, b; Pl. 10, fig. 1

A description of external and internal shell features was given by Benson (1959, p. 60). Diagnostic features are: elongate-subrectangular shape; dorsal margin nearly straight to slightly convex; ventral margin slightly concave; anterior margin broadly curved, slightly extended below, fringed with numerous small short spines; posterior margin narrower, subtruncate, bears three or four thick blunt spines below, and is slightly concave above.

Valves subequal, left slightly overreaching right in cardinal areas. Convexity moderate, greatest convexity posteromedian. Anterior margin with broad but steep-sided, sharp-crested rim; posterior margin with flattened but not appreciably elevated border. Median surface separated from free margins by a shallow groove, very narrow ventrally; a large, rounded anteromedian node and many small nodes and short ridges on valve surface.

Hinge of right valve consists of an anterior high pointed tooth; posterojacent socket, supported below by a spurlike extension from base of tooth; an interterminal narrow groove; and a posterior curved high tooth. Hinge of left valve comprises an anterior deep socket, posterojacent tooth from base of which a hook-shaped spur supports ventral part of socket and beneath which is an ocular sinus, an interterminal bar, and a posterior socket. Inner lamellae fairly broad, line of concresence and inner margin slightly separated anteriorly and posteroventrally; radial canals number about 20 anteriorly and 10 posteriorly, are sinuous, and in part occur in pairs. Adductor muscle scar formed of a curved subvertical row of four scars on posterior flank of median tubercle together with three additional scars in anterior flank of node (a somewhat unusual group of mandibular and antennal scars for podocopid ostracod).

Length of figured shell (Pl. 3, fig. 1b) 0.56 mm, height 0.30 mm, convexity of shell 0.28 mm.

Antennule with five segments beyond protopodite; proximal segment twice length of longest of other segments; distal and penultimate segments very narrow; third segment probably represents fusion of two segments, as dorsally it bears two distal setae and three median setae.

Antenna indistinctly segmented, consisting of only three podomeres, the second very long; terminal podomere with three short, stout claws; other portion of antennule with three ventral and two dorsal setae; exopodite reaching halfway to end of endopodite, three-segmented; ultimate segment crossmarked. Mandibular palp bears about five clawlike setae distally and two long setae on penultimate podomere. Maxillary palp has about 12 rays, each of which becomes suddenly thicker near base; rays smooth. Legs three-jointed above terminal claws.

REMARKS: The outline, general surface ornamentation, and internal structures of this form are similar if not identical to those of *P. rugipunctata* (Ulrich and Bassler, 1904, p. 118) from the Miocene to Recent of the Atlantic and Caribbean regions of North and Central America. Benson (1959, p. 60) believes the surface nodes of *P. pacifica* are less strongly developed than in *P. rugipunctata*. The latter species was assigned to *Carino-*

cythereis Ruggieri (Moore *et al.*, 1961, p. 341), but the present consensus among ostracode workers is that *rugipunctata* should remain in *Puriana*. The appendages are described here for the first itme.

OCCURRENCE: A common to abundant nearshore Recent species in Gulf of California, Station 39, depth 21 fathoms, muddy sand bottom; Station 41, depth 45 fathoms, sand bottom; Station 49, depth 390 fathoms, mud bottom; Station 53, depth 8 fathoms, sand bottom; Station 67, depth 4 fathoms, sand bottom; Station 77, depth 3 fathoms, sand bottom; Station 78, depth 10 fathoms, sand bottom; Station 87, depth 7 fathoms, sandy mud bottom; Station 88, depth 8 fathoms, gravel and sand bottom; Station 94, depth 4 fathoms, sand bottom; Station 102, depth 6 fathoms, sand bottom; Station 110, depth 10 fathoms, sand bottom; Station 111, depth 7 fathoms, hard clay bottom; Station 123, depth 5 fathoms, sandy mud bottom; Station 126, depth 20 fathoms, sandy mud bottom; Station 130, depth 62 fathoms, sandy mud bottom; Station 137, depth 7 fathoms, muddy sand bottom; Station 140, depth 15 fathoms, shell and sand bottom; Station 141, depth 10 fathoms, sand bottom; Station 143, depth 10 fathoms, sand bottom; Station 144, depth 75 fathoms, muddy sand bottom; Station 153, depth 18 fathoms, muddy sand bottom; Station 158, depth 17 fathoms, muddy sand bottom; Station 162, depth 13 fathoms, sand bottom; Station 173, depth 220 fathoms, muddy sand bottom; Station 175, depth 7.5 fathoms, sand bottom; Station 179, depth 488 fathoms, mud bottom; Station 180, depth 14 fathoms, sand bottom; Station 187, depth 13 fathoms, muddy sand bottom; Station 189, depth 10 fathoms, sand bottom; Station 192, depth 262 fathoms, mud bottom; Station 197, depth 28 fathoms, sandy mud bottom; Station 201, depth 13 fathoms, muddy sand bottom; Station 204, depth 40 fathoms, muddy sand bottom; Station 211, depth 10 fathoms, muddy sand bottom; Station 213, depth 8 fathoms, sand bottom; Station 216, depth 18 fathoms, sandy mud bottom; Station 217, depth 15 fathoms, sandy mud bottom.

NUMBER OF SPECIMENS STUDIED: 25 + (1 living)

Genus *Trachyleberidea* Bowen, 1953

Trachyleberidea tricornis Swain sp. nov.
(Fig. 54d; Pl. 5, fig. 7)

Shell elongate-subquadrate in side view, highest about one-fourth from anterior end; dorsal margin nearly straight, about three-fifths of shell length, with much more obtuse but less well-defined anterior than posterior cardinal angle; anterior cardinal margin slightly elevated; ventral margin nearly straight, converging with dorsum posteriorly; anterior margin broadly convex, somewhat extended below; posterior margin much narrower, extended medially, truncate above, bearing a few blunt spines below. Valves subequal, compressed, greatest convexity postventromedian.

Anterior margin of valve with broad, elevated margin rim and minutely spinose margin; anterior rim continues ventrally and posteriorly as an alaform ridge that terminates in a pointed node; an oblique declivity trends from end of alaform ridge toward posterodorsal cardinal area; surface sharply depressed posterior to declivity. Posterior margin with rim about equal in width to that of anterior margin but lower; a large, rounded anteromedian node is more abruptly defined posteriorly than anteriorly; posterior three-fifths of dorsal margin with an irregular, narrow submarginal ridge; a rounded ocular node present anterodorsally; general surface finely and closely pitted.

Hinge of left valve consists of an anterior rounded socket and posterojacent bluntly pointed tooth, interterminal slightly serrate bar, and posterior slightly elongate, deep socket. Inner lamellae moderately broad anteriorly, narrower ventrally and posteriorly, vestibule about one-fifth width of lamellae anteriorly; radial canals numerous and closely spaced terminally, fewer ventrally. Muscle scar not clearly seen in material at hand.

Length of holotype left valve 0.57 mm, height 0.30 mm, convexity of valve 0.17 mm.

RELATIONSHIPS: This species is similar to *Hermanites reticulata* Puri from Miocene of Florida in general form, surface pits and ridges, and hingement but is more elongate, more densely pitted, and has a more extended dorsal margin. It also conforms in general shell characteristics to *Trachyleberidea* Bowen except for a lack of development of median ridge and is tentatively referred to that genus.

OCCURRENCE: Recent, Gulf of California, Station 41, depth 45 fathoms, sand bottom; Station 88, depth 8 fathoms, gravel and sand bottom; Station 100, depth 38 fathoms, gravel and sand bottom, Station 143, depth 10 fathoms, sand bottom.

NUMBER OF SPECIMENS STUDIED: 7

Trachyleberidea? sp.
(Pl. 8, fig. 10)

Immature right valve of shell has following characteristics: subpyriform in side view, highest one-fourth from anterior end; dorsal margin fundamentally straight, but concave owing to projections of marginal ridges in cardinal areas; ventral margin gently convex, converging posteriorly toward dorsum; anterior margin broadly curved, slightly extended below, with four or five small spines ventrally; posterior margin acuminately pointed and spinose, strongly extended medially. Valve moderately convex, greatest convexity posteromedian; posterior sixth of valve markedly compressed.

Anterior and ventral margins of valve with narrow knife-edge ridge; posterior part of dorsal margin with narrow submarginal ridge that projects slightly beyond margin middorsally and strongly at posterior end of hinge. Anteromedially is a large, rounded swelling, defined posteriorly by a shallow, curved furrow; a prominent spine occurs posteroventrally at place of maximum convexity, and an obscure ridge extends anteriorly from spine; general surface coarsely reticulate; edges of reticulations are minutely spinose except in a small posteromedian area.

Hinge margin of immature right valve with weak, elongate, crenulate teeth and intervening weakly crenulate furrow; inner lamellae very narrow in immature valve; radial canals few and widely spaced, simple. Muscle scar a median vertical row of three or four small, closely spaced spots.

Length of figured right valve 0.45 mm, height 0.26 mm, convexity of valve 0.14 mm.

REMARKS: The general shape and surface ornamentation of this immature form are close to *Trachyleberidea*, but the hinge is too poorly developed and other features of the shell are too immature for classification. It is included here because of its unique characters.

OCCURRENCE: Recent, Gulf of California, Station 86, depth 30 fathoms, sandy mud bottom.

NUMBER OF SPECIMENS STUDIED: 1

Family XESTOLEBERIDEIDAE Sars, 1928
Genus *Xestoleberis* Sars, 1866

Xestoleberis hopkinsi Skogsberg
(Figs. 33a, b, 58a–h; Pl. 2, figs. 3a, b, 7, 8a–h, 9a, b)

Xestoleberis hopkinsi Skogsberg, 1950, California Acad. Sci. Occasional Papers, v. 26, no. 14, p. 492, Pls. 29, 30, figs. 1–16

Male shells: Subovate-pyriform outline, dorsum strongly convex with greatest height posteromedian, venter slightly concave anteromedially, anterior margin narrow extended below, posterior margin broadly curved; valves subequal, left valve larger than and extending slightly beyond edge of right dorsally and terminally; valves inflated in posterior half; surface smooth; hinge consists of a long, narrow interterminal rabbet

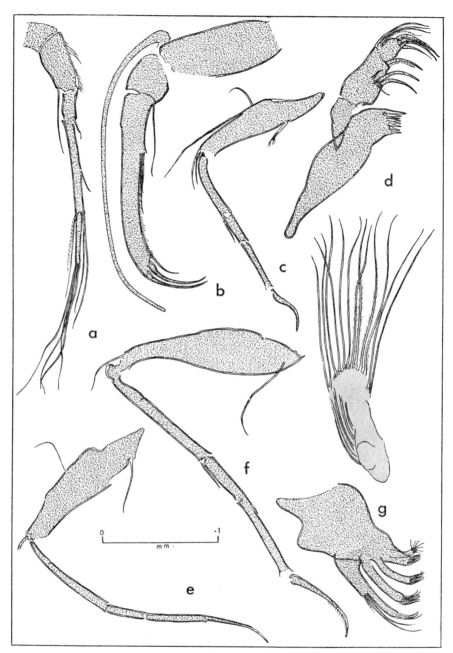

Figure 57. Loxocorniculum sculptoides *Swain sp. nov., Scammon Lagoon, Baja California.*
(a) Antennule; (b) Antenna; (c) First thoracic leg; (d) Mandible and palp;
(e) Second thoracic leg; (f) Third thoracic leg; (g) Maxilla and respiratory
lobe

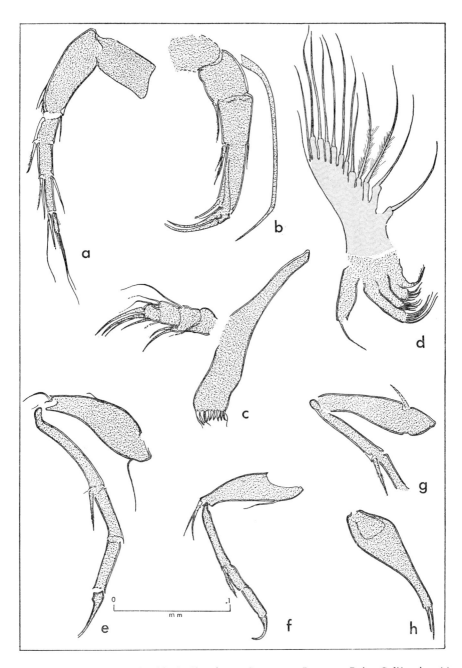

Figure 58. Xestoleberis hopkinsi *Skogsberg, Scammon Lagoon, Baja California.* (a) Antennule: (b) Antenna; (c) Mandible and palp; (d) Maxilla and respiratory lobe; (e) Third thoracic leg; (f) First thoracic leg; (g) Second thoracic leg; (h) Furca

groove in left valve for reception of edge of right valve, and terminal very weakly crenulate depressions in left valve into which fit crenulate, flangelike terminal ridges in right valve; inner lamellae of moderate width anteriorly, narrower ventrally and posteriorly; line of concrescence and inner margin separated, except anteromidventrally at position of selvage apophysis; radial canals short, about 18 anteriorly, fairly straight, bunched ventrally. Adductor muscle scar consists of an anteromedian subvertical row of four closely spaced spots; no other spots seen in specimens at hand.

Female shells: Shell elongate, subovate-reniform in side view, highest about one-third from posterior end; anterior margin narrowly rounded, extended below, curving sharply into ventral margin but merging gradually with dorsum; posterior margin broadly curved, extended medially, bending abruptly into ventral margin; dorsal margin moderately to strongly convex with steep posterior and more gradual anterior slope; ventral margin slightly convex anteromedially. Left valve slightly larger than right; valves moderately convex, greatest convexity posteromedian. Valve surfaces smooth. Internal features like those of males.

Antennule composed of five segments beyond basis, second and third penultimate segments each with an anterior distal strong seta; first penultimate segment with two such setae, and ultimate segment with two long setae.

Antenna with three poorly differentiated segments beyond basis; second segment short and broad with posterior distal seta; next segment comprises two fused segments, each portion with a posterior distal seta; ultimate podomere short and bears two strong distal claws; exopodite with articulation near distal end, not reaching quite to end of distal claws.

Mandible provided with about eight elongate teeth on cutting edge, in addition to which there are three distal setae; mandibular palp four-segmented; second segment with one outer and two inner distal setae; third segment with two outer and one inner setae; ultimate segment with two terminal strong claws.

Maxilla has five terminally setaceous lobes, of which outer is opposed to other four and has single distal seta; palp with comparatively few rays, about 12, each of which is enlarged near base.

First thoracic leg with second podomere as long as but much narrower than basis and with outer distal seta; basis with two distal setae; third and fourth segments shorter than others; terminal claw sharply curved forward. Second and third legs similar to first but longer. Furcal ramus small, with two terminal claws.

Length of a figured male specimen (Pl. 2, fig. 8f) 0.43 mm, height 0.28 mm, convexity 0.25 mm.

REMARKS: The shell and anatomical features of the present specimens conform to characters prescribed for *X. hopkinsi.* The forms from Baja California referred to *X. aurantia* (Baird) by Benson (1959, p. 55) may represent *X. hopkinsi.*

OCCURRENCE: Recent, Gulf of California, Station 41, depth 45 fathoms, sand bottom; Station 67, depth 4 fathoms, sand bottom; Station 69, depth 395 fathoms, mud bottom; Station 77, depth 3 fathoms, sand bottom; Station 88, depth 8 fathoms, gravel and sand bottom; Station 94, depth 4 fathoms, sand bottom; Station 102, depth 6 fathoms, sand bottom; Station 119, depth 31 fahoms, sand bottom; Station 126, depth 20 fathoms, sandy mud bottom; Station 137, depth 7 fathoms, muddy sand bottom; Station 143, depth 10 fathoms, sand bottom; Station 147, depth 6 fathoms, sand bottom; Station 156, depth 7 fathoms, sand bottom; Station 158, depth 17 fathoms, muddy sand bottom; Station 162, depth 13 fathoms, sand bottom; Station 173, depth 220 fathoms, muddy sand bottom; Station 179, depth 488 fathoms, mud bottom; Station 187, depth 13 fathoms, muddy sand bottom; Station 189, depth 10 fathoms, sand bottom; Station 192, depth 262 fathoms, mud bottom; Station 197, depth 28 fathoms, sandy mud bottom; Station 204, depth 35 fathoms, mud bottom.

NUMBER OF SPECIMENS STUDIED: 25 + (1 living)

Xestoleberis parahowei Swain sp. nov.
(Pl. 2, figs. 6a, b)

Shell elongate, subtriangular to subtrapezoidal in lateral view, highest medially; dorsal margin strongly convex, posterior slope a little steeper than anterior; ventral margin nearly straight; terminal margins narrowly rounded, extended below, the anterior slightly less pointed than posterior. Valves subequal, moderately convex, greatest convexity ventromedian. Ventral surface of shell flattened. Surface of valves smooth.

Hinge of right valve consists of terminal ridgelike teeth, each of which bears six to eight denticulations, and an intervening smooth furrow. Inner lamellae of moderate width anteriorly, narrower elsewhere; line of concrescence and inner margin separated terminally. Radial canals short, numbering eight to ten anteriorly. Adductor scar a median vertical row of four spots and two more-anterior spots, the dorsal of which is curved.

Length of holotype right valve (Pl. 2, fig. 6a) 0.33 mm, height 0.20 mm, convexity of valve 0.14 mm.

RELATIONSHIPS: The general shape, musculature, and hingement of this species relate it to *Xestoleberis* Sars. Among described species that have pointed ends, *X. depressa* Sars (1866, p. 68) and *X. setigera* Brady (1880, p. 125) are somewhat similar to the present species but are less pointed posteriorly. The characteristics of the species are like *X. howei* Puri, but the dorsum is less convex than in that species.

OCCURRENCE: Recent, Gulf of California, Station 21, depth 32 fathoms, mud bottom; Station 39, depth 21 fathoms, muddy sand bottom; Station 78, depth 10 fathoms, sand bottom; Station 87, depth 7 fathoms, sandy mud bottom; Station 112, depth 34 fathoms, hard clay; Station 123, depth 5 fathoms, sandy mud bottom; Station 179, depth 488 fathoms, mud bottom; Station 195, depth 75 fathoms, sandy mud bottom; Station 217, depth 15 fathoms, sandy mud bottom. A very similar species is *X. howei* Puri from the Miocene Chipola facies of the Alum Bluff beds, and the *Arca, Ecphora* and *Cancellaria* facies of the Choctawhatchee beds of Florida.

NUMBER OF SPECIMENS STUDIED: 14

Xestoleberis cf. *nana* Brady
(Pl. 2, fig. 4)

Xestoleberis nana BRADY, 1880, Challenger Reports, pt. 3, Ostracoda, p. 126, Pl. 31, figs. 5a–c

Left valve subelliptical in side view, highest posteromedially; dorsal margin moderately convex; ventral margin nearly straight; anterior margin narrowly rounded, extended below; posterior margin somewhat more broadly curved, also extended below. Valve moderately convex, greatest convexity posteromedian. Surface of valve smooth.

Hinge of left valve consists of terminal elongate, weakly crenulate furrows and an interterminal faintly grooved ridge formed of extended valve edge. Inner lamellae of medium width anteriorly, narrower ventrally and posteriorly; lamellae nearly parallel to plane of valve contact anteriorly, sloping steeply toward valve interior elsewhere; line of concrescence and inner margin separate. Radial canals few and widely spaced. Muscle scar a median vertical row of four spots not closely spaced and one or perhaps two more-anterior antennal spots.

Length of figured left valve 0.38 mm, height 0.22 mm, convexity of valve 0.13 mm.

REMARKS: The outline and smooth, strongly convex surface of this specimen closely resemble features of *X. nana* Brady from the South Pacific.

OCCURRENCE: Recent, Gulf of California, Station 143, depth 10 fathoms, sand bottom; Station 162, depth 13 fathoms, sand bottom; Station 179, depth 488 fathoms, mud bottom; Station 187, depth 13 fathoms, muddy sand bottom; Station 189, depth 10 fathoms, sand bottom.

NUMBER OF SPECIMENS STUDIED: 8

Subclass BRANCHIOPODA Calman, 1909
Order CLADOCERA Calman, 1909
Suborder EUCLADOCERA Eriksson, 1934
Superfamily CHYDOROIDEA Mattox, 1959
Family DAPHNIDAE Straus, 1820
Genus DAPHNIA Müller, 1785

Daphnia? sp.
(Pl. 1, fig. 9)

The illustration is of the ephippium of a probable *Daphnia*. Ephippium subovate with straight dorsal margin; anterior margin narrower than posterior, the latter extended below; egg pouch a single oval swelling, of which long axis is more or less parallel to dorsal margin. General surface smooth, surface of pouch densely pustulose.

Length of figured ephippium 0.43 mm, height 0.23 mm.

OCCURRENCE: At edge of lagoon near road from Esquinapa and Las Cabras, at km 13 from Esquinapa, Sinaloa, Mexico; salinity 42‰.

NUMBER OF SPECIMENS STUDIED: 3

REFERENCES CITED

Andel, T. H. van, and Shor, G. G., 1964, Marine geology of the Gulf of California: Am. Assoc. Petroleum Geologists, Mem. 3, Tulsa, 408 p.

Baird, W., 1850, The natural history of the British Entomostraca: London Roy. Soc., p. i–viii, 1–366, Pls. 1–36

Benson, R. H., 1959, Ecology of Recent Ostracodes of the Todos Santos Ray Region, Baja California, Mexico: Kansas Univ. Paleont. Contr., Arthropoda, art. 1, p. 1–80, Pls. 1–11, figs. 1–20

Benson, R. H., and Coleman, G. L., II, 1963, Recent marine ostracodes from the eastern Gulf of Mexico: Kansas Univ. Paleont. Contr., Arthropoda, art. 2, p. 1–52, Pls. 1–8, figs. 1–33

Benson, R. H., and Kaesler, R. L., 1963, Recent marine and lagoonal ostracodes from the Estero de Tastiota region, Sonora, Mexico (Northeastern Gulf of California): Kansas Univ. Paleont. Contr., Arthropoda, art. 3, p. 1–34, Figs. 1–20, Pls. 1–4

Bold, W. A. van den, 1946, Contribution to the study of Ostracoda, with special reference to the Tertiary and Cretaceous microfauna of the Caribbean region: Amsterdam, Univ. Utrecht Dissert., J. H. DeBussy, p. 1–157, Pls. 1–18

—— 1958, Ostracoda of the Brasso Formation of Trinidad: Micropaleontology, v. 4, p. 391–418, Figs. 1, 2, Pls. 1–5

—— 1963, Upper Miocene and Pliocene Ostracoda from Trinidad: Micropaleontology, v. 9, p. 361–424, Pls. 1–12

Brady, G. S., –?1868a, *in* Folin and Perier's Les Fonds de la Mer, v. 1, pt. 1, 163 p. 19 pls.

—— 1868b, A monograph of the Recent British Ostracoda: Linn. Soc. London. Trans., v. 26, p. 353–495, Pls. 23–41

—— 1880, Report on the Ostracoda dredged by *H.M.S. Challenger* during the years 1873–1876; Challenger Reports, Zoology, pt. 3, p. 1–184, Pls. 1–44

—— 1886, Notes on Entomostraca collected by Mr. A. Haly in Ceylon: Linn. Soc. Jour., v. 19, p. 293–317, Pls. 37–40

Brady, G. S., and Norman, A. M., 1889, A monograph of the marine and freshwater Ostracoda of the North Atlantic and Northwestern Europe: Roy. Dublin Soc. Sci. Trans., ser. 2, v. 4, p. 1–270, Pls. 8–23

Brady, G. S., and Robertson, D., 1869, Notes of a week's dredging in the west of Ireland: Ann. Mag. Nat. Hist., ser. 4, v. 3, p. 353–374, Pls. 18–22

—— 1872, Contributions to the study of the Entomostraca. VI. On the distribution of the British Ostracoda: Ann. Mag. Nat. Hist., ser. 4, v. 9, p. 48–70, Pls. 1, 2

Coryell, H. N., and Fields, S., 1937, A Gatun ostracode fauna from Cativa, Panama: Am. Mus. Novitates, no. 956, 18 p., 2 pls.

Crouch, R. W., 1949, Pliocene Ostracoda from Southern California. Jour. Paleontology, v. 23, p. 594–599, Pl. 96

Cushman, J. A., 1906, Marine Ostracoda of Vineyard Sound and adjacent waters: Boston Soc. Nat. Hist. Proc., v. 32, p. 359–385, Pls. 27–38

Edwards, R. A., 1944, Ostracoda from the Duplin Marl (Upper Miocene) of North Carolina: Jour. Paleontology, v. 18, p. 505–528, Pls. 85–88

Hartmann, G., 1957, Zur Kenntnis das Mangrove-Estero-Gebietes von El Salvador und seiner Ostracoden-Fauna: Kieler Meeresforschungen, v. 13, p. 134–159

—— 1959a, Beitrag zur Kenntnis des Nicaragua—Sees unter besonderer Berücksichtigung seiner Ostracoden: Zool. Anz., v. 162, p. 269–294

—— 1959b, Zur Kenntnis der lotischen Lebensreiche der pazifischen Kürte von El Salvador fauna. III. Beitrag zur Fauna El Salvador: Kieler Meeresforschungen, v. 15, p. 187–241

Howe, H. V., and Chambers, J., 1935, Louisiana Jackson Eocene Ostracoda: Louisiana Dept. Conserv., Geol. Bull. 5, p. 1–64, Pls. 1–4

Howe, H. V., and others, 1935, Ostracoda from the *Arca* zone of the Choctawhatchee Miocene of Florida: Florida Dept. Conserv., Geol. Bull. 13, p. 1–47, Pls. 1–4

Klie, W., 1940, Süsswasserostracoden aus Nordbrasilien. V. Die Gattung *Strandesia:* Zool. Anz., v. 129, p. 201–206, 8 figs.

LeRoy, L. W., 1943, Pleistocene and Pliocene Ostracoda of the coastal region of Southern California: Jour. Paleontology, v. 17, p. 354–373, Pls. 58–62

Malkin, D. S., 1953, Biostratigraphic study of Miocene Ostracoda from New Jersey, Maryland, and Virginia: Jour. Paleontology, v. 27, p. 761–799

Mincher, A. R., 1941, The fauna of the Pascagoula Formation: Jour. Paleontology, v. 15, p. 337–348, Pls. 46, 47

Moore, R. C., and others, 1961, Arthropoda 3, Pt. Q, p. i–xxiii, Q1–Q442, Figs. 1–344 in Treatise on invertebrate paleontology: Geol. Soc. America and Kansas Univ. Press

Müller, G. W., 1894, Die Ostracoden des Golfes von Neapel und der angrenzenden Meeres-Abschnitte: Naples Sta. Zool., F.u.F. Golfes Neapel, Mon. 21, p. 1–viii, 1–404, Pls. 1–40

Münster, G., 1830, Ueber einige fossile Arten Cypris (Müller, Lamarck) und Cythere (Müller, Latreille, Demarest), Neues Jahrb. für Min. Geol. Palaeontologie, for 1830, p. 60–67

Norman, A. M., 1864, Report of the Crustacea dredged off the coasts of Northumberland and Durham, 1862–1864: Nat. Hist. Soc. Northumberland and Durham Trans., v. 1, p. 12–29, Pls. 5–7

Puri, H. S., 1954, Contribution of the study of the Miocene of the Florida Panhandle: Florida Geol. Survey Bull. 36, 345 p., 17 pls.

Roden, G. J., and Groves, G. W., 1959, Recent oceanographic investigations in the Gulf of California: Jour. Marine Research, v. 18, p. 10–35

Rothwell, W. T., 1944, Preliminary ecological study of some Recent Pacific Ostracoda: Geol. Soc. America, Bull., v. 55, p. 1470 (abst.)

Sars, G. O., 1866, Oversigt af Norges Marine Ostracoder: Norske Vidensk.-Akad. forhandl. (1865), p. 1–130

Skogsberg, T., 1928, Studies on marine ostracods. II. External morphology of the genus Cythereis with descriptions of twenty-one new species: California Acad. Sci. Occasional Papers, v. 15, p. 3–154

Swain, F. M., 1952, Ostracoda from wells in North Carolina, pt. I, Cenozoic Ostracoda: U.S. Geol. Survey Prof. Paper 234–A, p. 1–58, 3 figs., Pls. 1–7

—— 1955, Ostracoda of San Antonio Bay, Texas: Jour. Paleontology, v. 29, p. 561–646, 39 figs., Pls. 59–64

—— 1963, Pleistocene Ostracoda from the Gubik Formation, Arctic Coastal Plain, Alaska: Jour. Paleontology, v. 37, p. 798–834, 13 figs., Pls. 95–99

Triebel, E., 1940, Die Ostracoden der deutschen Kreide. Cytherideinae und Cytherinae aus der Unteren Kreide: Senckenbergiana, v. 22, p. 160–227, 10 pls.

Ulrich, E. O., and Bassler, R. S., 1904, Systematic Paleontology, Miocene Arthropoda: Maryland Geol. Survey, Miocene Volume, p. 98–130, Pls. 35–38

Manuscript Received by the Society May 1, 1964

EXPLANATION OF PLATES

Plate 1. CYTHERELLIDAE, BAIRDIIDAE, CYPRIDIDAE, PARACYPRIDIDAE, AND CLADOCERA

Figures | Page

1. *Cytherelloidea californica* LeRoy 31
   Exterior of right valve, Station 201 (× 62)

2a–f. *Bairdia simuvillosa* Swain sp. nov. 34
   (a) Interior of paratype left valve, Station 143 (× 62); (b) Exterior of paratype right valve, same locality (× 62); (c) Exterior of holotype left valve, same locality (× 62); (d) Exterior of paratype right valve, same locality (× 62); (e) Exterior of paratype left valve, same locality (× 62); (f) Exterior of paratype right valve, same locality (× 62)

3a, b. *Potamocypris mazatlanensis* Swain sp. nov. 41
   (a) Dorsal view of paratype left valve, Station C-83 of Curray (× 56); (b) Interior of paratype left valve, same locality (× 56)

4. *Cyprinotus unispinifera* Furtos 38
   Exterior of immature right valve, Station C-83 of Curray (× 48)

5a, b. *Potamocypris mazatlanensis* Swain sp. nov. 41
   (a) Right side of holotype shell, Station C-83 of Curray (× 56); (b) Right side of paratype shell, same locality (× 56)

6a–d. *Bairdia verdesensis* LeRoy 36
   (a, b) Exterior views of right valves, Station 143 (× 45); (c) Interior of left valve, Station 67 (× 45); (d) Right side of complete shell, Station 143 (× 45)

7. *Cytherella ovularia* Swain sp. nov. 29
   Exterior of holotype right valve, Station 52 (× 56)

8. *Bairdia simuvillosa* Swain sp. nov. 34
   Exterior of paratype right valve, Station 143 (× 62)

9. *Daphnia?* sp. (Ephippium) 112
   Station C-80 of Curray (× 58)

10. *Stenocypria australia* Swain sp. nov. 40
   Interior of paratype left valve, Station C-80 of Curray (× 40)

11. *Cytherelloidea californica* LeRoy 31
   Exterior of immature right valve, Station 67 (× 62)

12. *Macrocyprina pacifica* (LeRoy) 42
   Exterior of right valve, Station 143 (× 41)

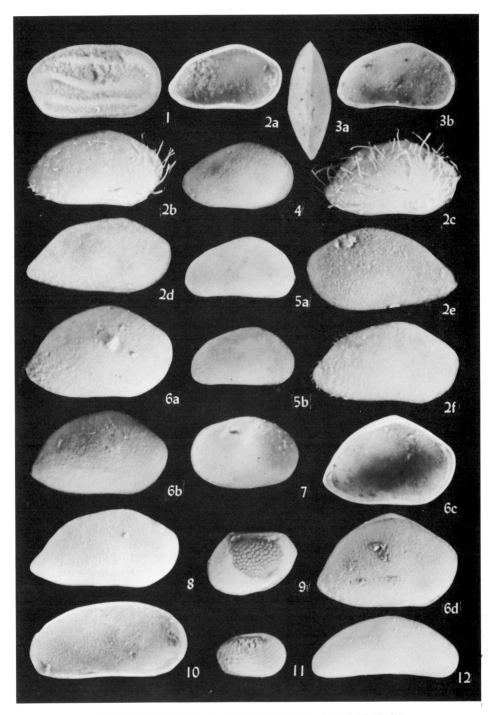

CYTHERELLIDAE, BAIRDIIDAE, CYPRIDIDAE,
PARACYPRIDIDAE, AND CLADOCERA

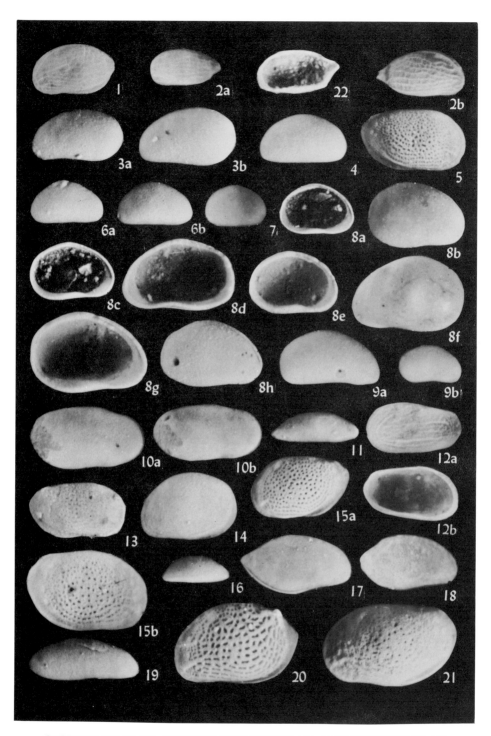

CYTHERURIDAE, XESTOLEBERIDEIDAE, LOXOCONCHIDAE,
LEGUMINOCYTHERIDAE, AND PARADOXOSTOMATIDAE

PLATE 3. TRACHYLEBERIDIDAE, HEMICYTHERIDAE, CYTHERIDAE, AND CYTHERURIDAE

Figures | Page

1a–c. *Puriana pacifica* Benson 105
(a) Interior of left valve, Station 67 (× 60); (b) Exterior of right valve, same locality (× 60); (c) Exterior of left valve, same locality (× 60)

2a, b. *Cativella dispar* Hartmann 102
(a) Right side of shell, Station 102 (× 60); (b) Exterior of right valve, same locality (× 60)

3a, b. *Pterygocythereis delicata* Coryell and Fields 47
(a) Exterior of right valve, Station 119 (× 64); (b) Exterior of broken left valve, same locality (× 48)

4a–c. *Pterygocythereis delicata* Coryell and Fields 47
(a) Exterior of immature right valve, Station 123 (× 60); (b) Exterior of immature right valve, same locality (× 60); (c) Exterior of immature right valve, same locality (× 60)

5a, b. *Orionina pseudovaughani* Swain sp. nov. 86
Exterior views of two immature left valves, Station 102 (× 65)

6a–d. *Pumilocytheridea vermiculoidea* Swain sp. nov. 51
(a) Left side of paratype shell, Station 189 (× 62); (b, c) Left side and dorsal views of holotype shell, same locality (× 62); (d) Right side of paratype shell, same locality (× 62)

7. *Pumilocytheridea* sp. 51
Exterior of immature? right valve, Station 67 (× 62)

8a, b. *Kangarina* cf. *quellita* Coryell and Fields 68
(a) Exterior of left valve, Station 143 (× 56); (b) Interior of left valve, same locality (× 56)

9. *Cytherura johnsonoides* Swain subspecies a? 63
Exterior of right valve, Station 102 (× 58); a specimen with caudal extension more ventrally placed than in holotype, and which may represent a subspecies

10. *Cytherura johnsonoides* Swain sp. nov. 62
Exterior of paratype right valve, Station 102 (× 58); a specimen with shorter caudal process than in holotype; or female?

11a–c. *Cytheropteron dobladoensis* Swain sp. nov. 68
(a) Exterior of holotype right valve, Station 143 (× 54); (b) Exterior of paratype left valve, same locality (× 54); (c) Exterior of paratype right valve, same locality (× 54)

12. *Cytherura johnsonoides* Swain sp. nov. 62
Exterior of holotype left valve, Station 67 (× 58)

13. *Orionina pseudovaughani* Swain sp. nov. 86
Exterior of holotype right valve, Station 119 (× 65)

14. *Costa?* cf. *variabilocostata seminuda* van den Bold 104
Exterior of right valve, Station 104 (× 60)

15. *Cativella unitaria* Swain sp. nov. 103
Exterior of holotype right valve, Station 123 (× 60)

TRACHYLEBERIDIDAE, HEMICYTHERIDAE, CYTHERIDAE,
AND CYTHERURIDAE

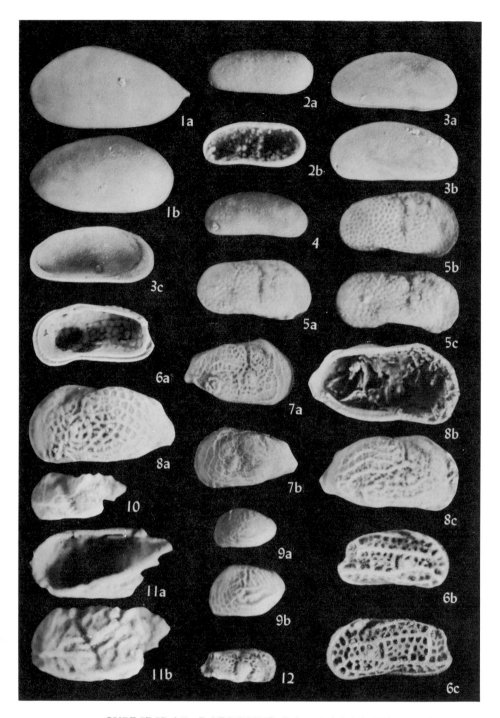

CYPRIDIDAE, DARWINULIDAE, PARACYPRIDIDAE,
LIMNOCYTHERIDAE, HEMICYTHERIDAE, CYTHERIDAE,
AND CYTHERURIDAE

SWAIN, PLATE 4

PLATE 4. CYPRIDIDAE, DARWINULIDAE, PARACYPRIDIDAE, LIMNOCYTHERIDAE, HEMICYTHERIDAE, CYTHERIDAE, AND CYTHERURIDAE

Figures — Page

1a, b. *Cyprinotus unispinifera* Furtos 38
(a) Exterior of mature valve, Station C-83 of Curray (× 48); (b) Exterior of mature right valve, same locality (× 48)

2a, b. *Darwinula yaquensis* Swain sp. nov. 46
(a) Exterior of holotype left valve, Station 111 (× 64); (b) Interior of paratype right valve, same locality (× 64)

3a–c. *Stenocypria australia* Swain sp. nov. 40
(a) Interior of paratype right valve, Station C-80 of Curray (× 40); (b) Exterior of paratype left valve, same locality (× 40); (c) Interior of holotype left valve, same locality (× 40)

4. *Aglaiocypris virgenensis* Swain sp. nov. 45
Exterior of holotype, a left valve, Station 197 (× 67)

5a–c. *Limnocythere sanctipatricii* Brady and Robertson 90
(a) Exterior of female right valve, Station C-80 of Curray (× 60); (b) Exterior of female right valve, same locality (× 60); (c) Exterior of male right valve, same locality (× 60)

6a–c. *Orionina pseudovaughani* Swain sp. nov. 86
(a) Interior of paratype right valve, Station 137 (× 48); (b) Exterior of paratype right valve, same locality (× 48); (c) Left side of paratype shell, same locality (× 48)

7a, b. *Perissocytheridea meyerabichi* (Hartmann) 53
(a) Exterior of immature right valve, Station C-80 of Curray (× 40); (b) Left side of immature shell, same locality (× 40)

8a–c. *Perissocytheridea meyerabichi* (Hartmann) 53
(a) Exterior of left valve, Station C-80 of Curray (× 40); (b) Interior of left valve, same locality (× 40); (c) Exterior of right valve (× 40); all female shells

9a, b. *Cytheropteron ventrokurtosa* Swain sp. nov. 65
(a) Exterior of paratype left valve, Station 123 (× 56); (b) Left side of paratype shell, Station 67 (× 56)

10. *Paracytheridea granti* LeRoy 70
Exterior of immature left valve, Station 143 (× 54)

11a, b. *Paracytheridea granti* LeRoy 70
(a) Interior of right valve, Station 143 (× 54); (b) Exterior of left valve, same locality (× 54)

12. *Paracytheridea? pichelinguensis* Swain sp. nov. 70
Exterior of holotype right valve, Station 67 (× 52)

PLATE 5. CYTHERIDAE, HEMICYTHERIDAE, AND TRACHYLEBERIDIDAE

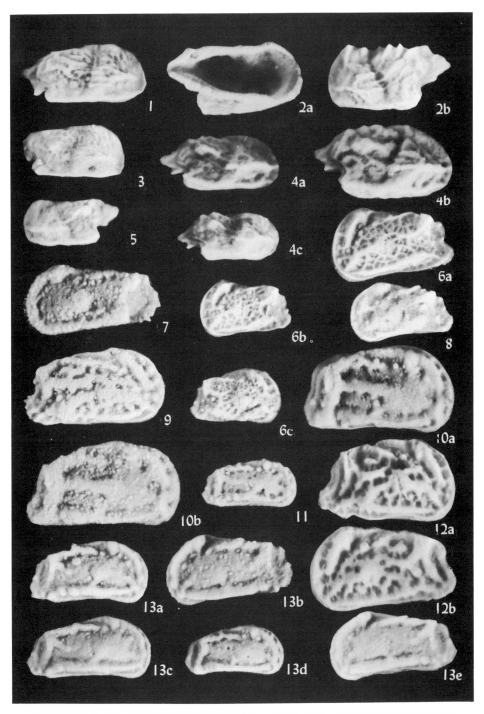

CYTHERIDAE, HEMICYTHERIDAE, AND TRACHYLEBERIDIDAE

SWAIN, PLATE 5

Geological Society of America Memoir 101

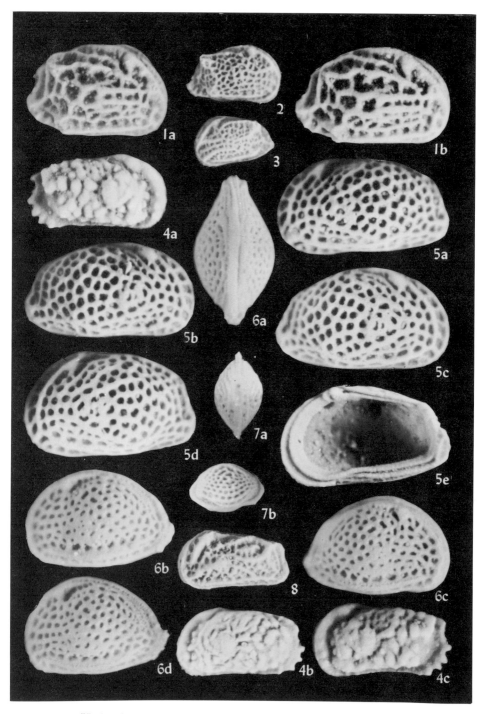

HEMICYTHERIDAE AND TRACHYLEBERIDIDAE

Plate 6. HEMICYTHERIDAE AND TRACHYLEBERIDIDAE

Figures Page

1a, b. *Mutilus confragosa* (Edwards) 83
Exterior views of two right valves, Station 143 (× 60)

2. *Hemicythere* sp. a 74
Exterior of immature right valve, Station 143 (× 60)

3. *Aurila conradi californica* Benson and Kaesler 77
Exterior of immature left valve, Station 143 (× 60)

4a–c. *Puriana pacifica* Benson 105
(a) Exterior of right valve, Station 137 (× 60); (b) Exterior of left valve, Station 67 (× 60); (c) Exterior of left valve, Station 137 (× 60)

5a–e. *Hemicythere californiensis* LeRoy 72
(a) Exterior of left valve, Station 153 (× 62); (b) Exterior of right valve, same locality (× 62); (c) Exterior of a right valve, higher with respect to length than (b), same locality (× 62); (d) Exterior of left valve, higher than (a), same locality (× 62); (e) Interior of right valve, same locality (× 62)

6a–d. *Aurila conradi californica* Benson and Kaesler 77
(a, b) Dorsal and left side views of shell, Station 137 (× 60); (c) Right side of shell, same locality (× 60); (d) Exterior of left valve, same locality (× 60)

7a, b. *Hemicythere* sp. b 74
(a) Left side of immature shell, Station 111 (× 54); (b) Dorsal view of immature shell, same locality (× 54)

8. *Ambostracon glauca* (Skogsberg) 76
Exterior of left valve of female?, Station 102 (× 48)

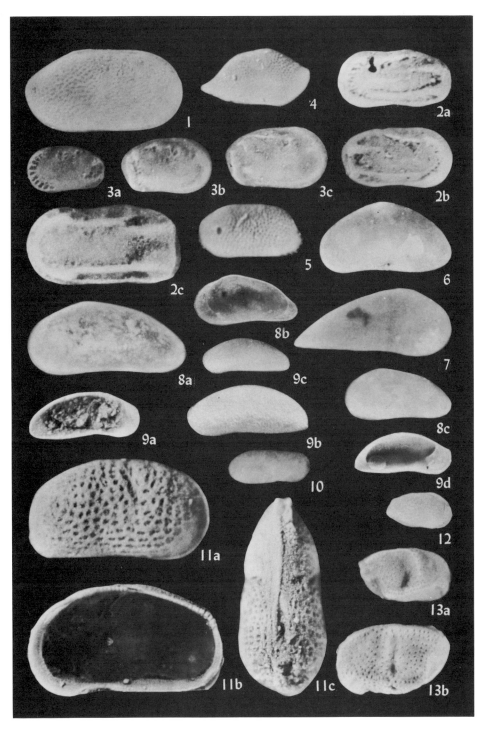

CYTHERELLIDAE, BAIRDIIDAE, PARACYPRIDIDAE,
PONTOCYPRIDIDAE, PARADOXOSTOMATIDAE,
CYTHERIDEIDAE, AND BYTHOCYTHERIDAE

SWAIN, PLATE 7

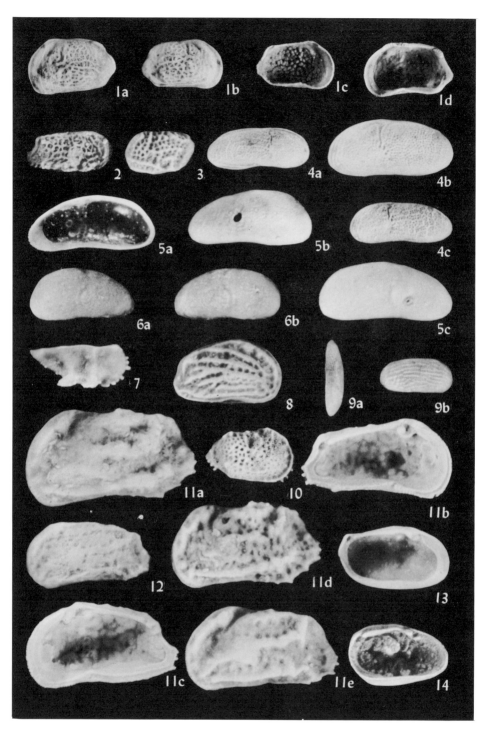

CYTHERIDAE, CYTHERURIDAE, LOXOCONCHIDAE,
CYTHERIDEIDAE, TRACHYLEBERIDIDAE, HEMICYTHERIDAE,
PARADOXOSTOMATIDAE, AND LEGUMINOCYTHERIDAE

SWAIN, PLATE 8

Plate 8. CYTHERIDAE, CYTHERURIDAE, LOXOCONCHIDAE, CYTHERIDEIDAE, TRACHYLEBERIDIDAE, HEMICYTHERIDAE, PARADOXOSTOMATIDAE, AND LEGUMINOCYTHERIDAE

Figures — Page

1a–d. *Perissocytheridea meyerabichi* (Hartmann) 53
(Male shells). (a) Exterior of left valve, Station C-80 of Curray (× 40); (b) Exterior of right valve, same locality (× 40); (c) Interior of immature left valve, same locality (× 40); (d) Interior of right valve, same locality (× 40)

2. *Paracytheridea? pichelinguensis* Swain sp. nov. 70
Exterior of paratype right valve, Station 67 (× 52)

3. *Pteroloxa guaymanensis* Swain sp. nov. 95
Left side of holotype shell, Station 130 (× 55)

4a–c. *Cushmanidea guardensis* Swain sp. nov. 58
(a) Exterior of paratype right valve, Station 78 (× 54); (b) Exterior of holotype left valve, same locality (× 54); (c) Exterior of paratype left valve, same locality (× 54)

5a–c. *Cushmanidea pauciradialis* Swain sp. nov. 57
(a) Interior of paratype female right valve, Station 140 (× 55); (b) Exterior of female paratype left valve, Station 78 (× 55); (c) Exterior of female holotype right valve, Station 162 (× 55)

6a–b. *Cushmanidea pauciradialis* Swain sp. nov. 57
(a) Exterior of immature or male right valve, Station 140 (× 55); (b) Exterior of immature or male left valve, same locality (× 55)

7. *Pterygocythereis? cuevasensis* Swain sp. nov. 48
Exterior of holotype right valve, Station 41 (× 56)

8. *Aurila convergens* Swain sp. nov. 79
Exterior of holotype right valve, Station 137 (× 57)

9a, b. *Megacythere punctocostata* Swain sp. nov. 99
(a) Exterior of holotype right valve, Station 78 (× 53); (b) Dorsal view of paratype right valve, same locality (× 53)

10. *Trachyleberidea?* sp. 107
Exterior of right valve, probably of immature specimen, Station 86 (× 54)

11a–e. *Ambostracon vermillionensis* Swain sp. nov. 75
(a) Exterior of paratype female left valve, Station 162 (× 51); (b) Interior of paratype male left valve, Station 140 (× 51); (c) Interior of paratype female right valve, same locality (× 51); (d) Exterior of a rugose paratype female left valve, Station 162 (× 51); (e) Exterior of holotype male left valve, Station 140 (× 51)

12. *Ambostracon vermillionensis* Swain sp. nov. 75
Exterior of a presumed immature left valve, Station 140 (× 51)

13. *Basslerites* sp. 89
Interior of left valve, Station 21 (× 28)

14. *Basslerites delrayensis* LeRoy 88
Interior of right valve, Station 41 (× 57)

PLATE 9. CYTHERIDAE, PARADOXOSTOMATIDAE, CYTHERURIDAE, BYTHOCYTHERIDAE, TRACHYLEBERIDIDAE, AND LOXOCONCHIDAE

Figures	Page
1. *Krithe producta* Brady	55
Exterior of left valve, Station 60 (× 54)	
2a, b. *Parakrithe?* sp.	56
(a) Interior of right valve, Station 204 (× 70); (b) Exterior of left valve, same locality (× 70)	
3a–c. *Parakrithella oblonga* Swain sp. nov.	56
(a) Interior of paratype right valve, Station 123 (× 60); (b) Exterior of paratype right valve, same locality (× 60); (c) Interior of holotype right valve, same locality (× 60)	
4a, b. *Cytherois* cf. *fischeri* (Sars)	97
Interior views of two left valves, Station 179 (× 70)	
5. *Paracytherois? perspicilla* (Benson and Kaesler)	97
Station 77 (× 70)	
6. *Sclerochilus? contortellus* Swain sp. nov.	98
Exterior of holotype right valve, Station 144 (× 70)	
7. *Cytherura bajacala* Benson	64
Right side of shell, Station 142 (× 72)	
8a–c. *Cytheropteron assimiloides* Swain sp. nov.	67
(a) Exterior of immature paratype right valve, Station 144 (× 54); (b) Exterior of immature paratype right valve, Station 216 (× 54); (c) Exterior of holotype right valve, Station 130 (× 54)	
9. *Cytheropteron caboensis* Swain sp. nov.	65
Left side of holotype, Station 21 (× 54)	
10. *Cytheropteron altatensis* Swain sp. nov.	64
Right side of holotype, Station 52 (× 54)	
11a–d. *Cytheropteron ventrokurtosa* Swain sp. nov.	65
(a) Right side of holotype shell, Station 102 (× 56); (b) Exterior of paratype right valve, Station 143 (× 56); (c) Right side of paratype, Station 140 (× 56); (d) Interior of paratype right valve, Station 41 (× 56)	
12. *Miracythere?* sp.	49
Exterior of left valve of probably immature specimen, Station 25 (× 56)	
13. *Costa? sanfelipensis* Swain sp. nov.	104
Exterior of holotype right valve, Station 217 (× 58)	
14a–c. *Xiphichilus tenussimoides* Swain sp. nov.	98
(a) Interior of holotype right valve, Station 39 (× 55); (b) Exterior of paratype right valve, Station 153 (× 55); (c) Exterior of paratype left valve, broken posteriorly, Station 39 (× 55)	
15. *Cytheromorpha* sp. aff. *C. warneri* Howe and Spurgeon	94
Right side of shell, Station 197 (× 56)	
16a, b. *Ambostracon glauca* Skogsberg	76
(a) Exterior of immature left valve, Station 162 (× 48); (b) Ventral view of paratype right valve, same locality (× 48)	
17a–d. *Cytherura paracostata* Swain sp. nov.	60
(a) Interior of paratype female? right valve, Station 175 (× 60); (b) Exterior of holotype right valve, same locality (× 60); (c) Interior of paratype right valve, same locality (× 60); (d) Ventral view of paratype shell, same locality (× 60)	
18a, b. *Loxoconcha? emaciata* Swain sp. nov.	92
(a) Exterior of holotype right valve, Station 189 (× 48); (b) Exterior of paratype left valve, same locality (× 48)	

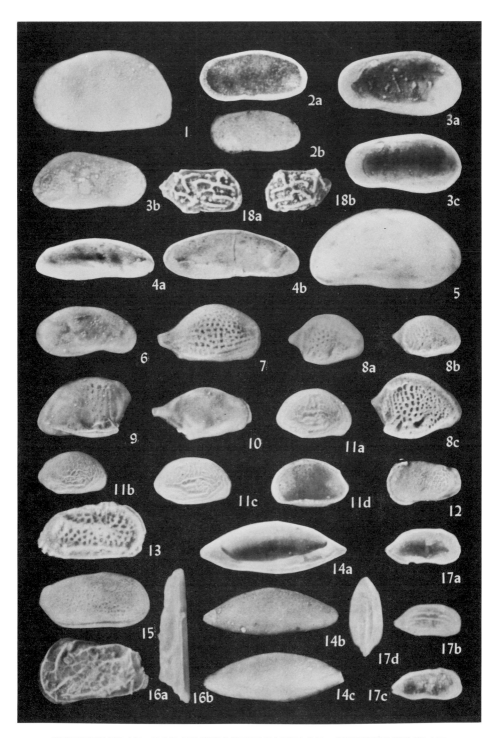

CYTHERIDAE, PARADOXOSTOMATIDAE, CYTHERURIDAE,
BYTHOCYTHERIDAE, TRACHYLEBERIDIDAE,
AND LOXOCONCHIDAE

SWAIN, PLATE 9

INDEX

Numbers in **boldface** refer to detailed descriptions.

135